LIBERTY TREE

Fourth Edition

A Beka Book® Pensacola, FL 32523-9100
an affiliate of PENSACOLA CHRISTIAN COLLEGE®

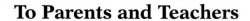

To Parents and Teachers

Children are eagerly searching for a workable sense of values. They need reading material that will give them ideals to reach for and examples to follow.

The stories in this reader have been selected from the readers of America's past and have been edited, modernized, and classroom-tested for student appeal and readability. Many character values are woven throughout the stories. Thought questions at the end of the stories aid in understanding the selections.

Liberty Tree
Fourth Edition

Staff Credits
Editors: Laurel Hicks, Marion Hedquist
Designer: Michelle Johnson
Illustrators: Brian Jekel and staff

Credits: "For All," reprinted by permission of Harold Ober Associates Incorporated. Copyright © 1951 by Eleanor Farjeon.

"Ladi," copyright by Bible Visuals International, P.O. Box 153, Akron, PA 17501-0153. Copyright 1966, 1994. Used by permission.

Photo Credits: page 10–top-courtesy of Corbis Corporation, bottom-Digital Vision; 26–Jupiterimages; 27, 32–The Granger Collection, New York; 34–Digital Vision; 74–Jupiterimages; 138-Dynamic Graphics; 186-background Corel, girls Jupiterimages; 187–Jupiterimages.

Cataloging Data
        Liberty tree / editor: Laurel Hicks, Marion Hedquist
    240 p. : col. ill. ; 22 cm. (A Beka Book reading program)
    1. Readers (Primary) 2. Reading (Primary) III. Hicks, Laurel. IV. Hedquist, Marion.
V. A Beka Book, Inc.
Library of Congress PE1119 .L53 2008

Contents

Pronunciation Key

Symbol • Example		Symbol • Example	
ā	āte	ŏ	nŏt
â	dâre	oi	boil
ă	făt	o͞o	fo͞od
ä	fäther	o͝o	bo͝ok
ə	ago (ə·gō′)	ou	out
ē	ēven	th	thin
ĕ	ĕgg	th	there
ê (ər)	pondĕr	tu̯	pictu̯re
ī	īce	ū	ūnit
ĭ	ĭt	û	hûrt
ō	ōver	ŭ	ŭp
ô	côrd, taught, saw	zh	measure

Liberty Tree

Eager voices raised a charge,
"People should be free!"
Men agreed and soon became
The Sons of Liberty.

"To meet within a building's walls
Alerts the enemy,
But no one would suspect some men
Talking by a tree."

Thus at a tree began the war,
The fight for liberty.
And from its boughs were proudly hung
The banners of the free.

Soon the rousing news was spread
Across the colonies.
Many men joined in the fight
And chose their Liberty Trees.

And just as brave hearts then were stirred
By banners in a tree,
My heart is stirred to see unfurled
The flag that waves for me.

—*Tracy Glockle*

Elizabeth Irvine's Ride

Alberta Walker/Mary R. Parkman

Think not of your weakness but
the strength of your cause; not of your
danger but the greatness of the service
which you can render; not of your hard-
ships, but of your glorious chance to
live and die fighting the good fight.

Elizabeth Ann was a bright, black-eyed girl
who lived in Virginia long years ago when
the beautiful Shenandoah Valley was covered with
forests instead of smiling farmlands as it is today.
She loved to play about under the great trees with
her brothers and sisters, and she often longed to ride
along the western trail that led over the mountains.

"Some day I shall ride and ride into the blue hills
of the sunset," she said. But she knew that dangers
lurked in the wild country beyond their plantation
at Deerfield. At night she could hear the howling
of wolves in the woods and there were, besides, the
Indians. From the time she was a very little girl, she
had been used to seeing them filing over the trail
in their bright blankets and moccasins. Sometimes
they looked very fierce in paint and feathers. They
always seemed wild and strange.

Shenandoah (shĕn′ən·dō′ə)

One day when Elizabeth was a little girl about eight years old, the children were playing merrily in the woods. Suddenly an old Indian woman stepped out from behind a tree and said, "Me Shawnee Kate—much hungry." While the other children hid away in fright, Elizabeth came running back, her little pinafore filled with cornpone and apples.

pinafore—*a sleeveless, apronlike garment*
cornpone—*flat bread made of ground corn*

After that, Shawnee Kate appeared again and again. Sometimes she would nod to Elizabeth and pass by without speaking. Sometimes she would ask for a drink from the well.

Elizabeth would bring her something to eat and say, "It must be a hungry walk over the hills. Some day I am going along the trail, and maybe then you will give me something by your campfire."

"Kate not forget," said the Indian woman.

The years passed and Elizabeth did go over the trail—to a home of her own. The day came when she put her hand in Francis Irvine's and went with him to the clearing called Long Glade. She rode away on her horse, Dundee, a present from her father.

"I have often longed to ride this way," she said to her young husband; "and now it is truly my trail— the way to my new home."

The days at Long Glade were happy and busy. There was no time to be lonely, not even when she was alone in the cabin from morning till night. She sang as she spun her linen and carded the wool that was to make clothes for herself and her husband. The pewter plates, too, that shone like silver on the dresser, proved her a good housewife.

---

pewter—*made of an alloy of tin
with lead, brass, or copper*

One day her husband said, "We are all going on a long hunting trip. It is just the time to get our winter's supply of venison. If we don't get our share now, Kill Buck's braves will not leave a deer on the mountain."

For the first time, the new home seemed very lonely. Young Mrs. Irvine found herself thinking all that afternoon, as she wove her wool and linen into stout linsey-woolsey, of the days when she had played with her sisters about the old home at Deerfield.

A shadow fell across the doorway. There was an Indian woman standing there.

"Why, Kate!" cried Elizabeth in amazement. "I thought you were with your people at South Branch. I didn't know you were in this part of the country. Come in and rest."

"No rest," said the old woman. "I come to tell you. Kill Buck makes ready get scalps Deerfield."

Elizabeth raised her hand toward the great dinner horn. Then she remembered; all the men of the little settlement were away chasing deer on the mountain. She looked out to where the western sun was dropping behind the trees. It was thirty miles to Deerfield; it would be dark before she could go half the way. There was no time for waiting and think-

venison—*deer meat*
linsey-woolsey—*cloth made from linen
  and wool or cotton and wool*

ing. There was but one thing to do. She ran to the pasture lot. "Dundee! Dundee! Come, Dundee!" she called. The horse galloped up, whinnying joyfully as she held out the bridle and buckled the saddle firmly on his back. "It's for Deerfield, Dundee!" she called to him softly, bending low over his neck as they started along the trail.

"It's a rough trail," she said to herself, as the horse stumbled in the gathering dusk, "but it's *my* trail, and God will bring us safely through the dark."

Thirty miles is indeed a long way over a rough forest road. Darkness had closed about her before she left the headwaters of the Glade. It was midnight when she came to the first mountain path, Buffalo Gap. Dundee had to feel his way, dodging rocks and stumps. With his wonderful "horse sense" he kept to the trail in spite of the briary undergrowth and overhanging branches that jealously struggled to cover up the man-made way through the wilderness.

Now an owl hooted directly overhead. Again and again came the howls of wolves disturbed by the strange invasion of the dark forest. Elizabeth shivered as she thought that some of Kill Buck's Indians might be hiding there, too.

There were eight more miles to go after the passing at Buffalo Gap. Elizabeth bent over and patted

---

briary—*full of briars; prickly*

her horse's neck. "Good Dundee," she said, "you'll
take me safely, I know."

All at once the horse almost stopped, then
plunged suddenly forward into a stream of running
water.

"Oh, Dundee, we're at Calf Pasture River and
we're almost home!" cried Elizabeth. The road was
all well known now, and Dundee cantered on with
renewed strength.

---

canter—to ride at an easy gallop

At last, just as the morning star appeared over the Blue Ridge, Dundee and his rider came within sight of Deerfield. "Weeping may last for a night, but joy comes in the morning," thought Mrs. Irvine.

She had reached her old home, and the settlement was saved.

Character Theme—Courage, Gratitude, & Kindness

Thinking It Through

1. What was Elizabeth's girlhood dream?

2. With what duties did Elizabeth occupy her day in her new home?

3. Why did Shawnee Kate warn Elizabeth about the Indian attack?

4. Did Shawnee Kate ever forget the kindness that Elizabeth showed her when Elizabeth was a child?

5. Why were no men sent to warn the people in Deerfield?

6. How did Elizabeth show bravery and courage?

The Best Do

Love the beautiful,
 Seek out the true,
Wish for the good,
 And the best do!
—*Mendelssohn*

Pass It On

Have you had a kindness shown?
 Pass it on!
'Twas not given for thee alone,
 Pass it on!
Let it travel down the years,
Let it wipe another's tears,
Till in heaven the deed appears—
 Pass it on!
—*Henry Burton*

The Arrogant Geese

Russian Fable

A peasant was one day driving some geese to town where he hoped to sell them. He had a long stick in his hand and drove them pretty fast. But the geese did not like to be hurried and happening to meet a traveler, they poured out their complaints against the peasant.

"Where can you find geese more unhappy than we? See how this peasant is hurrying us this way

and that and driving us just as though we were only common geese. Ignorant fellow! He never thinks that he is bound to respect us, for we are the descendants of the very geese that saved Rome so many years ago."

"But for what are you famous yourselves?" asked the traveler.

"Because our ancestors—"

"Yes, I know. I have read all about it. What I want to know is, what have you yourselves done?"

"Why, our ancestors saved Rome!"

"Yes, yes! But what have you done?"

"We? Nothing—"

"Of what good are you then? Do leave your ancestors at peace! They were honored for their deeds; but you, my friends, are only fit for roasting."

Character Theme—Humility

A War Story

Stella C. Shetter

No man can choose what coming hours may bring
To him of need, of joy, of suffering;
But what his soul shall bring unto each hour
To meet its challenge—this is in his power.
                                    —*Priscilla Leonard*

Well, well," said Grandma one evening when Bobby and Alice and Pink came to her room for a story, "I don't know what to tell you about tonight."

"Tell us a war story," suggested Bobby, eagerly.

"Maybe I might tell you a war story," agreed Grandma, "a war story of a time long ago." And she picked up her knitting and began slowly:

"When the Civil War broke out I was a very little girl. Of course there had been lots of talk of war, but the first thing I remember about it was when we heard that Fort Sumter had been fired on. It was a bright, sunshiny morning in the spring. I was helping Father rake the dead leaves off the garden when I saw a man coming up the road on horseback. I told Father, and he dropped his rake and went over the fence. In those days it wasn't as it is now. News traveled slowly—no telephones, no trains, no cars.

And this young man, who had been to Clayville to get his marriage license, brought us the news that Fort Sumter had been fired on.

"Father went straight into the house to tell Mother, and after a while he and my big brother, Joe, saddled their horses and rode away. I thought they were going right off to war, and I started to cry, and then I laughed instead when our big Dominique rooster flew up on the henhouse roof, flapped his wings, and crowed and crowed. A great many men and boys rode by our house that day on their way to Clayville, and when Father and Joe came back next day, Joe had volunteered and been accepted, and he stayed at home only long enough to pack his clothes and say good-bye to us.

"There wasn't much sleep in our house that night, and I lay in my trundle bed, beside Father and Mother's bed, and listened to them talking, talking, until I thought it must surely be morning. I went to sleep and wakened again and they were still talking. Finally I could hear Father's regular breathing and knew that he had gone to sleep at last. In a little bit Mother slipped out of bed and went into the hall. I thought she was going for a drink and followed her, but she went into Stanley's room, which had been Joe's room, too, until that night.

Dominique (däm′ə·nēk′)—*a chicken with yellow legs and gray, striped feathers*
trundle bed—*a low bed on rollers*

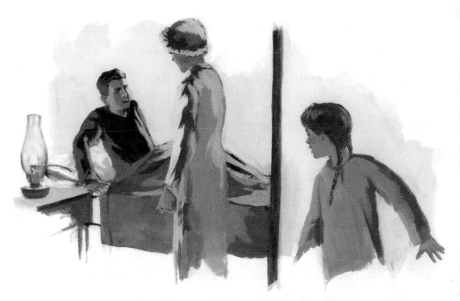

"Mother bent over Stanley and spoke his name softly, and he wakened and started up in his bed.

" 'What is it, Mother?' he whispered, frightened.

" 'Stanley,' Mother said slowly, 'I want you to promise me that you won't go to war without my consent.'

"Stanley laughed out loud in relief.

" 'Mother, you gave me a scare!' he said. 'I thought someone was sick or something. The war will be over long before I'm old enough to go.' He was going on sixteen then.

" 'It won't do any harm to promise, then,' Mother persisted, and Stanley promised.

"I crept back to bed and pulled the covers up over my head.

persist—*to refuse to give up*

"But Stanley was mistaken about the war being over soon. The war didn't stop. It went on and on. Two years and more passed, and Stanley was eighteen. Boys of that age were being accepted for service, but Stanley never said a word about volunteering.

"Shortly after his eighteenth birthday there came a change in him. He was not like himself at all. He had always been a lively boy, full of fun and mischief, but now he was very quiet. He never mentioned the war any more, and often dashed out of the room when everyone was talking excitedly about the latest news from the battlefield. He avoided the soldiers home on furlough, didn't seem to care to read Joe's letters, and as more and more of his friends enlisted, he became gloomy and downhearted.

"We could all see as time went on that Father was disappointed in Stanley. He was always saying how much better it was for a man to enlist than to wait to be drafted. The very word 'draft' had for Father a disgraceful sound.

"I think Mother must have thought it was Stanley's promise to her that was worrying him, for one day she came out to the barn where Stanley

---

furlough—*a leave of absence*
enlist—*to volunteer to serve in the military*
drafted—*required to serve in the military*

was shelling corn and I was picking out the biggest grains to play 'Fox and Geese' with. Mother told Stanley she released him from his promise, but he didn't seem glad at all. He only said, 'Don't you worry, Mother, I'm not going to war.'

" 'I was troubled about Joe that night,' Mother said. 'I thought I couldn't bear for you to go, too. But you are older now and you must do what you think best.'

"As Mother went out of the barn there were tears in her eyes, and I knew in that moment that she would rather have Stanley go to war than have him afraid to go.

"They were forming a new company in Clayville, and one day two recruiting officers came out to Nebo Cross Roads. Father let Truman take Charlie and me over to see them. It was raining, and I can see those two men yet standing there in the rain. One had a flute and the other had a drum. They played reveille and taps and guard mount and 'The Star-Spangled Banner' and a new song we had never heard before, 'Tenting on the Old Camp Ground.' How that music stirred the folks! They had to use two wagons to haul the recruits into Clayville that night.

"That evening when I was hunting eggs in the barn, I found Stanley lying face down in the hay.

---

reveille (rĕv′ə·lē)—*a bugle signal early in the morning*

He was crying! I could hardly believe my eyes.
I went a little nearer and I saw for sure that his
shoulders were shaking with sobs. But even while
I watched him he got to his feet and began rubbing his right arm. I often saw Stanley working
with his right arm. He would rub it and swing
it backward and forward and strike out with his
fist as if he were going to hit someone a blow. He
didn't mind my watching him, and I never told
anyone about it. He had broken that arm the winter before, and I had often seen him working with
it after he had stopped wearing it in a sling.

"I wondered to myself why, if Father and
Mother thought Stanley was afraid to fight, they
did not ask him and find out. He
knew why he didn't enlist—he

could tell them. At last I decided if they wouldn't do it themselves I'd do it for them. So the next time I was alone with Stanley, I said, 'Stanley, are you afraid to go to war?'

" 'Afraid!' he cried angrily, 'Who said I was afraid?' Then his tone changed. 'They don't want me. They won't have me. It's this arm,' and he held his right arm out and looked at it in a disgusted sort of way. 'They claim it's stiff, but I could shoot if they would only give me a chance. I've tried three times to get in, but there's no use worrying Mother about it since I can't go. But my arm is getting better. It's not nearly as stiff as it was. I'll get in yet." Then he looked at me scornfully and said, 'Afraid! Afraid nothing!'

"I ran as fast as ever I could to find Father and Mother and tell them. Mother hugged me and laughed and cried at the same time and said she always knew it, and Father made me tell over to him three times, word for word, every single thing Stanley had said.

" 'He must never know,' Mother said. 'He must never suspect for a minute that we thought he didn't want to go, the poor dear boy, keeping his trouble to himself for fear of worrying us.' And she told me to get Charlie and catch a couple of chickens to fry for supper. Then I knew she was happy again, for whenever Mother was happy or especially pleased with one of us, she always had something extra good to eat."

Thinking It Through

1. How old was Grandma when this story took place?

2. From what town did the news come? What was the news?

3. What did Mother ask Stanley to do?

4. After time went by, what did Mother and Father think was the reason for Stanley's not enlisting?

5. How did Grandmother help Stanley?

Bless This House

Bless this house, O Lord, we pray,
Make it safe by night and day;
Bless these walls, so firm and stout,
Keeping want and trouble out;
Bless the roof and chimneys tall,
Let thy peace lie over all;
Bless this door, that it may prove
Ever open to joy and love.

Who Patriots Are

Charles F. Dole

The course of history shows that many
a time a strong, earnest soul has swayed the
destiny of nations.   —*Dorothea S. Kapplin*

Who are the patriots in America? No
doubt many would answer at once: "The
patriots are the men who fought for their country
in times of war."

But there is something wrong in thinking that
patriots must be soldiers and sailors. What shall
we call the thousands of women who sent their
brothers and sons to help the cause of liberty?
Were not these women as good patriots as their
husbands and brothers? Indeed, the women often
had the hardest time. They had to carry on the
farms while the men were away; they suffered
from anxiety and loneliness. We must surely call
all brave women patriots who love the country well
enough to let their husbands and sons go to war for
the sake of the flag.

We must not forget a multitude of men who,
even in the War for Independence and in the great
Civil War, were never soldiers or sailors, and yet

---

multitude—*a large number*

were patriots. There was Benjamin Franklin, for instance. He did not fight, but who loved America better than he? There was Washington's friend, Robert Morris of Philadelphia, who helped get money to pay the soldiers. Where, in the time of war, would all the wheat and beef come from to feed the army, and the clothing to keep the men warm, if there were no patriots hard at work on their farms and in their shops?

We must not forget another set of good patriots in the times of Bunker Hill and Valley Forge. They were the patriot children who were not yet old enough to fight for their country, but who were perfectly willing to do so if they had been wanted. They helped their mothers and sisters while their fathers were away. They were full of gladness, too, when at last the long war was over, and later they passed on to their children the stories that their fathers had told to them about the heavy cost that had purchased our liberties.

To be a patriot is to love one's country. It is to be ready and willing, if need comes, to die for the country, as a good seaman would die to save his ship and his crew. It is to be just and fair and wise, and so to live nobly for our country.

To love our country, to work to make it strong and rich, to support its government, to obey its laws, to pay fair taxes into its treasury, to treat our fellow citizens as we like to be treated ourselves—this is to be good American patriots.

Thousands of brave patriots are risking their lives every day to help people and to save us all from harm. Brave doctors and nurses go where deadly disease is, and are not afraid to help save the sick. Brave sailors are always facing the sea and the storm. Brave firefighters stand ready to die to bring little children safely out of burning buildings.

Wherever we see a brave man, woman, or child, there we look for a patriot. Whoever is

---

live nobly—*to live bravely without shame*

brave to help others will be brave also for the sake of his country. Never forget it: it is better to be brave to help people than it is to be brave to harm them.

Character Theme—Courage, Patriotism, & Sacrifice

Thinking It Through

1. Are only soldiers patriots? Who are the patriots?

2. Why do women often have the hardest time during war?

3. How were children patriots during the War for Independence?

4. Who are some of the brave people who help our country in time of peace?

America's Gifts

President Herbert Hoover

My country owes me no debt. It gave me, as it gives every boy and girl, a chance. It gave me schooling, independence of action, opportunity for service and honor. In no other land could a boy from a country village without inheritance or influential friends look forward with unbound hope. My whole life has taught me what America means. I am indebted to my country beyond any power to repay.

Character Theme—Gratitude & Patriotism

---

influential—*important; powerful*
indebted—*owing gratitude*

JEFFERSON'S TEN RULES

President Thomas Jefferson

Never put off until tomorrow
what you can do today.

Never trouble another for what you
can do yourself.

Never spend your money before
you have earned it.

Never buy what you don't want
because it is cheap.

Pride costs more than hunger, thirst,
and cold.

We seldom repent of having eaten too
little.

Nothing is troublesome that we do
willingly.

How much pain the evils have cost us
that have never happened.

Take things always by the smooth
handle.

When angry, count ten before you
speak; if very angry, count
a hundred.

Character Theme—Self-Discipline

The
Honest Indian

An Old Indian Tale

Our character is but the stamp on our
souls of the free choices of good and evil
we have made through life.   *—Geikie*

An old Indian once bought some things from
a white man who kept a store.

When he got back to his wigwam, and opened his
bundle, he found some money inside it.

"Good luck!" thought the old Indian to himself, "I
will keep this money. It will buy many things."

He went to bed, but he could not sleep. All night
long he kept thinking about the money.

Over and over again, he thought, "I will keep it."
But something within him seemed to say, "No, you
must not keep it; that would not be right."

Early the next morning, he went back to the
store.

"Here is some money," said he. "I found it in my
bundle."

"Why did you not keep it?" asked the storekeeper.

"There are two men inside of me," replied the
Indian.

"One said, 'Keep it. You found it. No one will ever know.'

"The other said, 'Take it back! Take it back! It is not yours! You have no right to keep it!'

"Then the first one said, 'Keep it! Keep it!'

"But the other kept saying, 'No, no! Take it back! Take it back!'

"The two men inside of me talked all night. They would not let me sleep.

"I have brought the money back. Now the two men will stop talking. Tonight I shall sleep."

Character Theme—Honesty & Self-Discipline

Thinking It Through

1. Why could the Indian not sleep?

2. Did he know what was the right thing to do? What was his battle?

3. Why would he be able to sleep the next night?

Washington Stands Guard

O n one of the raw days in autumn in that dreadful winter at Valley Forge, Washington came out of his house and saw the sentinel on his doorstep. The maids were airing the house, and the general had stepped out for a moment. The soldier looked cold and hungry. Washington noticed it and said to him, "Have you had your breakfast yet?"

"No, your excellency. They are a little slow in relieving sentry this morning."

"Well," said Washington, "I'll relieve you. Let me have your musket. You go in and tell Mrs. Washington to give you a good hot breakfast and do not hurry back."

The soldier did as he was told. When he returned to his post to resume his duties, he found Washington still patiently standing guard over his own headquarters.

Character Theme—Humility & Service

sentinel—*soldier standing guard*   musket—*long-barreled gun*

Theodore Roosevelt

F ew men have been as popular as Theodore Roosevelt. There was something in
his wonderful sympathy that appealed to everyone
who knew him and to the millions who could only
read about him. Like Abraham Lincoln, he loved
the common people. Lincoln said, "The Lord must
love common people because He made so many of
them." Neither of these two great leaders set himself apart from the great mass of people. When
they spoke, the people recognized the voice of real
friends.

"I am a sounding board," Roosevelt used to say.
"How can I help in this good cause?" Truly he was
a sounding board that, before the days of television
and radio, echoed throughout the land. Crooked
deals fled before his denunciation; corrupt leaders
were driven from office; clean young men were encouraged to take part in political life.

A study of the lives of the great men of the world

sounding board—*a person who gives advice
about other people's ideas*
denunciation—*strong condemnation of evil*

shows hardly one able to do as many different things supremely well as Theodore Roosevelt. He was one of the most forceful and convincing public speakers of his day. He wrote many books that are still read with keenest interest. He was a thorough student of nature and loved all outdoor life. When he was leading his regiment in Cuba during the Spanish War, he astonished his officers by naming rare birds in the jungles. He was a successful soldier, a skillful politician, one of our greatest Presidents, and, more important, an example of righteous living to all the millions of people in our country.

Character Theme—Honesty & Integrity

Thinking It Through

1. How were Abraham Lincoln and Theodore Roosevelt alike?

2. The author says that crooked deals fled before his denunciation. What does that mean?

3. What lasting contribution did Theodore Roosevelt make to America?

My First Job

Andrew Carnegie (adapted)

An idle man said he could not find
bread for his family. "Neither can I,"
said an industrious man standing near.
"I have to work for all the bread I get."

In 1900, Andrew Carnegie was the owner of the world's largest steel company, and he was one of the richest men in the world. This wealthy American did not worship his money, however; he gave most of it away. He donated hundreds of millions of dollars to churches, schools, colleges, and public libraries. His generosity set an example for other wealthy men and women to follow.

What was this generous man like when he was a boy? Was life easy for him, or did he have to work for what he had? In this story you can find out by reading his own words.

When I was born, my father was a well-to-do master-weaver in Scotland. He owned four looms and employed apprentices. This was before the days of steam factories for the manufacture of linen. A few large merchants took orders and employed master-weavers, such as my father, to weave cloth; the merchants supplied the materials.

As the factory system developed, handloom weaving naturally declined, and finally there was no more work for my father to do. I was just about ten, and I resolved then and there that poverty should be driven from our door some day.

My parents decided to move to the United States and join relatives already in Pittsburgh. They thought the change would be a great sacrifice for them, but they made the decision because "it would be better for our two boys."

If you can look back when you are old as I do and wonder at the complete surrender of their own desires which parents make for the good of their children, you will reverence their memory.

When we arrived in the United States, Father started work at a cotton factory. I soon followed, and served as a "bobbin boy." This is how I began my preparation as a businessman. I received one dollar and twenty cents a week, and was then just about twelve years old.

I cannot tell you how proud I was when I received my first week's earnings. One dollar and twenty cents,

---

apprentice—*a person learning a craft or trade*

made by myself and given to me because I had been of some use in the world! No longer was I entirely dependent upon my parents, but at last I was able to be of help to them! I think this makes a man out of a boy sooner than almost anything else. It is everything to feel that you are useful.

Many millions of dollars have since passed through my hands, but the genuine satisfaction I had from that one dollar and twenty cents outweighs any later pleasure in money-getting. It was the direct reward of honest, manual labor; it represented a week of very hard work. For a lad of twelve to rise and breakfast every morning except the Sabbath, go into the streets and find his way to the factory, begin work while it was still dark outside, and not be released until after darkness had come again in the evening (with forty minutes at noon for lunch) was a terrible task.

People moan about poverty as a great evil and think that if people only had plenty of money, they

manual labor—*work with one's hands*

would be happy and useful and get more out of life. Yet if you will read the list of the world's most famous people, you will find that most of them were born poor and learned early how to work hard to help themselves and others.

Character Theme—Family, Industry, & Initiative

Thinking It Through

1. Where was Andrew Carnegie born?

2. Why did he have to begin work when he was very young?

3. What sacrifice did the parents make for their boys? How did Andrew feel about the sacrifice?

4. What was Andrew Carnegie's first job?

5. What makes a man out of a boy sooner than anything?

6. Did Andrew Carnegie believe that having plenty of money will make people happy?

Isaac Newton:
Discoverer of God's Laws

Laurel Hicks

Ten-year-old Isaac Newton eased the back door of the English farmhouse shut. As he raced through the tall grass on his way to the apple orchard, he felt the morning dew on his legs. He stopped for a moment to examine the funnel-shaped webs of the grass spiders, and he smiled at the cheerful singing of the songbirds. What a wonderful world his God had made!

Isaac stooped here and there to examine the wildflowers that grew in the orchard and in the woods beyond. "Here is a kind I don't have yet!" he thought, and he gathered a colorful bunch for his collection.

He was down by the stream now, watching frogs leap out of his way as he launched the model sailboat he had been working on for the past three days. This was not a model from a kit, but was entirely the work of his own hands. He watched as the force of wind and water carried the boat downstream. Then he raced along the bank to catch up with his model.

Isaac (ī′zĕk)

If only he had a better understanding of the forces
that make things go!

The scolding of squirrels and the slant of the
sun through the trees reminded Isaac that it was
almost time to return to the house for breakfast. He
skipped a flat stone across the surface of the water
and then chose two particularly beautiful pebbles to
take back with him.

Stopping in the barn, Isaac hung his flowers up-
side down from a nail to let them dry. Before enter-
ing the house, he checked the sundial he had carved
from wood a year earlier and had carefully mounted
to the outside of the building. Yes, it was just before
8:00, and time to be inside. He marveled at the order

in God's creation. "Even the sun obeys the rules God has set up for it," he thought. As he thanked God for the good breakfast his grandmother had prepared, he added a word of thanks for the marvelous design of the world about him.

After breakfast, Isaac took the pebbles up to his room and carefully arranged them on one of the shelves he had put up for his collections. He planned where he would display the flowers once they had dried. Then he checked his wooden models to make sure that the wheels of the carts still turned, the doors of the little houses still opened, and the water mill still spun at his touch.

Isaac took a tattered Bible from its shelf and sat on the edge of his bed. This Book had belonged to his father, who had died three months before Isaac's birth. Isaac opened to the book of Daniel, his favorite. He read all the way through to the last chapter and then sat wondering for a while about the time when "many shall run to and fro, and knowledge shall be increased" (Dan. 12:4). Isaac did not know that before too many years he would play a gigantic part in the increase of man's knowledge about the design of the universe. He did know, though, that he loved God's Word, he loved God's world, and he loved these summer days of freedom. If only summer vacation could last forever!

But of course it could not, and neither could his days on the farm. When Isaac was 11 or 12, his mother and stepfather realized that he had learned all that the small village school could teach him. He must go to a larger town for further studies. His Uncle William arranged for him to room with a pharmacist in Grantham while he attended King's School there. His mother hated to see Isaac go, but she knew that she and his grandmother had taught him well from the Scriptures. Isaac loved God, and God would watch over him.

In Grantham, Isaac was given the large attic of the house over the pharmacy for his bedroom. There was plenty of room here for his growing collections and for the drawings he loved to work on. There were books, too—books he had never read before—and the pharmacist gave him permission to use them. And there was the pharmacy below, with row after row of bottles containing crushed plants, oils, spices, minerals, and chemicals.

In the new school, Isaac studied arithmetic, history, Latin, logic, Bible, and art. Bible class was his favorite, and his teacher marveled at the way Isaac could memorize verse after verse of Scripture.

After classes were over, Isaac made more models, found ways to make new colors of paint from plants

---

pharmacist—*a druggist*
Latin—*the language of the ancient Romans*

logic—*the science of correct reasoning*

and minerals, and covered a wall of his room with his drawings. He worked with the pharmacist in the shop, rolling pills, mixing chemicals, and asking question after question. God had created a wonderful, orderly world, and Isaac wanted to know all he could about it so he could know more about God. In a notebook he wrote down his thoughts, his discoveries, and his unanswered questions.

A windmill was being built on the edge of town, and Isaac spent time after school watching the workmen and studying and measuring the work. Before long, he had made an exact model of the windmill, only much smaller. First he

mounted it outside his attic window and watched as the force of the wind turned the sails. Then he thought of a wonderful idea. He brought the model back inside and trained a mouse to run on a treadmill. As the mouse ran, it caused the miniature grinding stones to turn and grind small amounts of wheat into flour. "This is my miller," Isaac explained. "The only problem is that he eats more than he grinds!"

When Isaac was 18, he went off to study at Cambridge University, taking with him nothing but a bundle of clothes and his father's old Bible. He graduated in 1665 and would later become a professor at Cambridge.

Soon after Isaac's graduation, Cambridge closed down for a while because of a terrible plague called the Black Death, and Isaac went home to his mother's farm. He did not waste his time during this unexpected vacation. In just eighteen months between 1665 and 1667, Isaac Newton made great discoveries that have changed man's understanding of the universe.

He showed that the laws of gravity are true not only on our earth, but throughout the entire universe, and he stated the laws of motion. He showed that white light is not the absence of color but is made up of all the colors of the rainbow. He

---

Cambridge (kām′brĭj)

invented the kind of telescope that we use today, and he invented a new branch of mathematics, called calculus. All this he accomplished before he was 25 years old. Isaac Newton's boyhood attempts to learn more about God by gaining a better understanding of God's creation bore such fruit that today he is remembered as the greatest scientist who ever lived.

Despite his success as a scientist, and despite all the honors people gave to him, Sir Isaac Newton remained humble. Shortly before his death at the age of 84, he summed up his life in these words:

> I seem to have been only like a boy playing on the seashore. I have amused myself by now and then finding a smooth pebble or a pretty shell, but the great ocean of truth still lies before me unknown and unexplored.

This great man who discovered so much about the universe never lost his faith in the Creator of all things. He believed that this powerful Being not only made all things, but is "Lord of all."

Character Theme—Beauty, Faith, & Resourcefulness

---

telescope—*a scientific instrument that makes distant objects appear nearer*

Thinking It Through

1. How old was Isaac Newton when this story begins?

2. How did Isaac tell the time?

3. What book did he love?

4. Why did Isaac leave home?

5. How did he learn things?

6. How did Isaac's curiosity help him to become a great scientist?

7. Name some of the things Isaac Newton helped mankind understand.

From the Bible

The heavens declare the glory of God; and the firmament sheweth his handiwork.

—Psalm 19:1

A Tale of a
Forest Fire

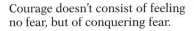

Courage doesn't consist of feeling
no fear, but of conquering fear.

C hildren, I will dismiss you now. The air
is becoming so thick with smoke that I
am afraid forest fires have broken out far off. Go
home as quickly as you can." So spoke Miss Nelson, the teacher of a school in northern Ontario.
It was about three o'clock in the afternoon, and in
less than two minutes the schoolhouse was empty.

For six weeks there had been little or no rain.
Fire had broken out in the forest in different places,
but as the weather had been calm, it had not
spread, but had quickly burned itself out. Now,
however, wind had sprung up, fire had broken out
again, and great clouds of smoke were already
blowing over the schoolhouse.

When the children separated and went off in
different directions, one little party of three took a
road leading north. These were Mabel Howard, a
girl of sixteen, and the two brothers, Tim and Harry

Ontario (än·tĕr′ē·ō)

Lennox, aged eleven and nine years. The parents of these children lived three miles from the school-house on adjoining farms, which were not likely to be reached by the fires; so the young people had no fear for the safety of their own homes.

They trudged cheerily on until they came to a belt of forest about half a mile broad, through which their road lay. Here the smoke was becoming dense, but the children, not expecting that the flames could reach so far, entered the wood without fear. They had not gone a hundred yards when the heat became unbearable; and, borne down by the westerly breeze, a roaring sound, like the rushing of mighty waters, fell upon their ears. Soon the hissing and crackling of the flames told them that the fire was fast sweeping toward them.

"Back—back to the clearing! We can't get through!" cried Mabel, turning to run.

Then, stopping as suddenly as she had started off, she exclaimed, "Oh, those poor children, Gertrude and Crissy Moore! I met their mother this morning, and she told me that she and Mr. Moore would be away from home all day, and the children would be alone. The house is two miles from here, and close to the woods. The fire will soon reach

---

adjoining—*neighboring*
trudge—*to walk*

dense—*thick*

the house, and the poor little girls will be burned to death!

"Come, boys, come! We must outrun the fire and get there in time to save them. Let us make a race for it!" And the three set off along the fields by the edge of the forest.

They started at full speed, and soon found that they were outstripping the flame. But great billows of smoke were rolling all around them, and before they had gone three-quarters of a mile the two boys sank to the ground, overcome by the heat, and almost stifled by the smoke.

What was to be done? Mabel could not leave them there in the path of the fire; and yet she dared not delay. Looking around in dismay and terror, her eyes fell on a well-known landmark—a small placid lake.

"Come, boys," she cried; "try again. Our lives and the lives of the Moore children depend upon our not giving way. The lake is just beyond us there. Hold tight to me, and I'll take you to it." And, half dragging the nearly unconscious lads, she brought them at last to the water's edge.

All three threw themselves down and drank as they had never drunk before. Then the boys declared they were ready to go on. But Mabel said, "No, lie down on the ground. The smoke will not reach you there; and if the fire creeps across the field, wade out into the lake, where you will be quite safe till I come back for you."

The boys lay down as she bade them, and then the heroic girl pushed on alone. Through the delay the fire had gained on her, and as she raced on in front of the roaring flames, she had to halt and stoop low to the earth to get a breath of pure air.

At last, breathless with running, Mabel reached Mr. Moore's farm. The two little children were clinging to each other, screaming for help. No time was

---

placid—*calm*

to be lost. The awful sea of fire was already bursting through the trees! Gently laying the children face down upon the ground, Mabel dipped her light woolen shawl in a pail of water, drew it over her head, and ran swiftly to the well at the back of the house.

The ready-witted girl lowered the bucket rapidly to the bottom, and drawing it up again empty, found that the water must be less than two feet deep.

The air was now so hot, that in order to breathe, she had to draw a fold of the wet shawl over her mouth and nose. While doing this, she noticed a pile of firewood standing in the yard. Hurrying to it, she brought back an armful of blocks, which she threw into the well. This action she repeated, until, letting down the bucket again, she found that the blocks of wood stood above the level of the water.

Running back to the house, she tore the blankets from the beds, snatched little Crissy up in her arms, and bidding Gertie hold on to her frock, hurried again to the well. To drop the blankets to the bottom, place the children, one at a time, in the bucket and lower them down, was the work of a few moments. Then letting the bucket remain below, she grasped the rope, slid down hand over hand, and joined the terrified children in their strange place of refuge.

---

refuge—*safety*

The descent was made not a moment too soon.
The flames were already rushing over the dry grass
and stubble. In another minute the rest of the wood-
pile was ablaze, and a sheet of flame swept over
the well. The rope, catching fire at the top, quickly
burnt through, and fell plump upon the heads of the
children.

---

descent—*a going down*

For hours they cowered in terror, watching the whirling smoke, and listening to the roaring flames above. By and by the noise grew less, the smoke cleared; and, quite worn out, Mabel and her little charges fell asleep.

At last Mabel was awakened by Crissy's plaintive cry, "I want my breakfast!" and found that the sun had risen upon another day. It was impossible to get out of the well. Mabel, though her heart was full of fear, did her best to comfort the little ones, hoping that at last someone would rescue them.

Several hours passed away. The sun had risen high in the heavens, when at last hurried footsteps were heard approaching. The anxious mother had reached her home, to find nothing but charred and glowing embers. A cry of despair broke from her when she could find no trace of her children.

But what is that? Her cry is answered by a faint shout! She stands eagerly listening. Again the shout is repeated—it sounds like a voice from the ground. A sudden thought strikes her. She rushes to the well, leans over the charred curb, and from the depths the cheering words reach her ears: "It's I, Mabel Howard. Gertrude and Crissy are with me."

Kneeling down by the brink, and peering into the darkness, Mrs. Moore caught a faint glimpse of

---

cower—*to huddle up in fear*   **plaintive**—*mournful; sad* the children, and uttered a glad cry of thankfulness. Then, opening a little parcel of cloth she had bought in the town, she tore the cloth into strips, and tied a number of them together. Fastening a stone to one end of the line she lowered it to Mabel, who quickly tied the rope to it. Then Mrs. Moore drew up the rope and fastened it to the windlass.

"Send the baby up first!" she cried joyfully. In a few moments the delighted little one appeared in the bucket at the mouth of the well, and was clasped in her mother's arms. Gertrude came next, and then Mrs. Moore exclaimed: "What shall we do now, Mabel? You are such a heavy lump of goodness that I'm afraid I can't wind you up."

"Never mind me," laughed Mabel, cheerily. "Just lower the bucket again and let me send up the blankets, and then I will make my own way out."

Up came the blankets; the bucket made another descent, and Mabel, grasping the rope with both hands, and leaning far back, planted her feet firmly against the rough wall, and walked up to daylight as cleverly as any boy could have done.

Imagine the words of heartfelt thankfulness with which she was greeted by the fond mother. Imagine, too, Mabel's joy when, on reaching home, she found that the little Lennox boys whom she had left at the

---

windlass—*part of a well, used for pulling up the bucket*

lake had also escaped unhurt. Mr. Moore's house was soon rebuilt, and in his best room hangs the portrait of the brave girl to whose courage and quick wit he owed the safety of his children, the sunshine of his home.

Character Theme—Adventure, Courage, & Service

Thinking It Through

1. Why did the fires not spread at first?

2. Why were Mabel, Tim, and Harry not worried?

3. When the boys could not travel any farther, what did Mabel do?

4. Why were the boys safe by the lake?

5. Why did Mabel throw the wood down into the well?

6. How did Mabel show courage?

A Boy's Prayer

Give me clean hands,
　clean words,
　and clean thoughts.

Help me to stand for the hard right
　against the easy wrong.

Save me from habits that harm.

Teach me to work as hard
　and play as fair in Thy sight alone
　as if all the world saw.

Forgive me when I am unkind,
　and help me to forgive those
　who are unkind to me.

Keep me ready to help others
　at some cost to myself.

—*William DeWitt Hyde*

Character Theme—Integrity &
Self-Discipline

The Emperor's New Clothes

Hans Christian Andersen

Many years ago there was an Emperor who was so excessively fond of new clothes that he spent all his money on them. He cared nothing about his soldiers, nor for the theater, nor for driving in the woods except for the sake of showing off his new clothes. He had a costume for every hour in the day. Instead of saying as one does about any other king or emperor, "He is in his council chamber," the people here always said, "The Emperor is in his dressing room."

Life was very merry in the great town where he lived. Hosts of strangers came to visit it every day, and among them one day were two swindlers. They gave themselves out as weavers and said that they knew how to weave the most beautiful fabrics imaginable. Not only were the colors and patterns unusually fine, but the clothes that were made of this cloth had the peculiar quality of becoming invisible to every person who was not fit for the office he held, or who was impossibly dull.

---

excessively—*too much*   swindler—*a person who cheats*

"Those must be splendid clothes," thought the Emperor. "By wearing them I should be able to discover which men in my kingdom are unfitted for their posts. I shall distinguish the wise men from the fools. Yes, I certainly must order some of that stuff to be woven for me."

The Emperor paid the two swindlers a lot of money in advance, so that they might begin their work at once.

They did put up two looms and pretended to weave, but they had nothing whatever upon their shuttles. At the outset they asked for a quantity of the finest silk and the purest gold thread, all of which they put into their own bags while they worked away at the empty looms far into the night.

"I should like to know how those weavers are getting on with their cloth," thought the Emperor, but he felt a little strange when he reflected that anyone who was unfit for his post would not be able to see it. He certainly thought that he need have no fears for himself, but still he thought he would send somebody else first to see how it was getting on. Everybody in the town knew what wonderful power the stuff possessed, and everyone was anxious to see how dull his neighbor was.

"I will send my faithful old minister to the weavers," thought the Emperor. "He will be best able to see how the stuff looks, for he is a clever man and no one fulfills his duties better than he does."

So the good old minister went into the room where the two swindlers sat working at the empty loom.

"Heaven help us," thought the old minister, opening his eyes very wide. "Why, I can't see a thing!" But he took care not to say so.

Both the swindlers begged him to be good enough to step a little nearer, and asked if he did not think it a good pattern and beautiful coloring. They pointed to the empty loom. The poor old minister stared as hard as he could, but he could not see anything, for of course there was nothing to see.

"Good heavens," thought he. "Is it possible that I am a fool? I have never thought so, and nobody must know it. Am I not fit for my post? It will never do to say that I cannot see the stuff."

"Well, sir, you don't say anything about the stuff," said the one who was pretending to weave.

"Oh, it is beautiful—quite charming," said the minister, looking through his spectacles. "Such a pattern and such colors! I will certainly tell the Emperor that the stuff pleases me very much."

"We are delighted to hear you say so," said the swindlers, and then they named all the colors and described the peculiar pattern. The old minister

paid great attention to what they said, so as to be able to repeat it when he got home to the Emperor.

Then the swindlers went on to demand more money, more silk, and more gold, to be able to proceed with the weaving. But they put it all into their own pockets. Not a single strand was ever put into the loom, but they went on as before, weaving at the empty loom.

The Emperor soon sent another faithful official to see how the stuff was getting on and if it would soon be ready. The same thing happened to him as to the minister. He looked and looked, but as there was only the empty loom, he could see nothing at all.

"Is not this a beautiful piece of stuff?" said both the swindlers, showing and explaining the beautiful pattern and colors which were not there to be seen.

"I know I am no fool," thought the man, "so it must be that I am unfit for my good post. It is very strange, though. However, one must not let it appear." So he praised the stuff he did not see, and assured them of his delight in the beautiful colors and the originality of the design.

"It is absolutely charming," he said to the Emperor. Everybody in the town was talking about this splendid stuff.

Now the Emperor thought he would like to see it while it was still on the loom. So, accompanied by a number of selected courtiers, among whom were the two faithful officials who had already seen the imaginary stuff, he went to visit the crafty impostors, who were working away as hard as ever they could at the empty loom.

"It is magnificent," said both the honest officials. "Only see, Your Majesty, what a design! What colors!" And they pointed to the empty loom,

---

impostor—*a person who pretends to be someone else*

for they each thought no doubt the others could see the stuff.

"What!" thought the Emperor. "I see nothing at all. This is terrible! Am I a fool? Am I not fit to be Emperor? Why, nothing worse could happen to me!"

"Oh, it is beautiful," said the Emperor. "It has my highest approval." And he nodded his satisfaction as he gazed at the empty loom. Nothing would induce him to say that he could not see anything.

The whole suite gazed and gazed, but saw nothing more than all the others. However, they all exclaimed with His Majesty, "It is very beautiful." And they advised him to wear a suit made of this wonderful cloth on the occasion of a great procession which was just about to take place. "Magnificent! Gorgeous! Excellent!" went from mouth to mouth. They were all equally delighted with it. The Emperor gave each of the rogues an order of knighthood to be worn in their buttonholes and the title of "Gentleman Weaver."

The swindlers sat up the whole night before the day on which the procession was to take place, burning sixteen candles, so that people might see how anxious they were to get the Emperor's new clothes ready. They pretended to take the stuff off the

---

suite (swēt)—*a group (of servants)*   procession—*a parade*
rogue—*a rascal; scoundrel*

loom. They cut it out in the air with a huge pair of scissors, and they stitched away with needles without any thread in them.

At last they said, "Now the Emperor's new clothes are ready."

The Emperor with his grandest courtiers went to them himself, and both swindlers raised one arm in the air, as if they were holding something. They said, "See, these are the trousers. This is the coat. Here is the mantle," and so on. "It is as light as a spider's web. One might think one had nothing on, but that is the very beauty of it."

"Yes," said all the courtiers, but they could not see anything, for there was nothing to see.

"Will Your Imperial Majesty be graciously pleased to take off your clothes?" said the impostors. "Then we may put on the new ones, along here before the great mirror."

The Emperor took off all his clothes, and the impostors pretended to give him one article of dress after the other of the new ones which they had pretended to make. They pretended to fasten something around his waist and to tie on something. This was the train, and the Emperor turned round and round in front of the mirror.

"How well His Majesty looks in the new clothes! How becoming they are!" cried all the people round.

"What a design, and what colors! They are most gorgeous robes."

"The canopy is waiting outside which is to be carried over Your Majesty in the procession," said the master of the ceremonies.

"Well, I am quite ready," said the Emperor. "Don't the clothes fit well?" Then he turned round again in front of the mirror, so that he should seem to be looking at his grand things.

The chamberlains who were to carry the train stooped and pretended to lift it from the ground with both hands, and they walked along with their hands in the air. They dared not let it appear that they could not see anything.

Then the Emperor walked along in the procession under the gorgeous canopy, and everybody in the streets and at the windows exclaimed, "How beautiful the Emperor's new clothes are! What a splendid train! And they fit to perfection!" Nobody would let it appear that he could see nothing, for then he would not be fit for his post, or else he was a fool.

None of the Emperor's clothes had been so successful before.

"But he has got nothing on," said a little child.

---

canopy—*a rooflike covering*

"Oh, listen to the innocent," said his father. And one person whispered to the other what the child had said. "He has nothing on—a child says he has nothing on!"

"But he has nothing on!" at last cried all the people.

The Emperor writhed, for he knew it was true. But he thought, "The procession must go on now." So he held himself stiffer than ever, and the chamberlains held up the invisible train.

Character Theme—Honesty & Humility

writhed—*squirmed*

Thinking It Through

1. What did the Emperor love more than anything else?

2. What was special about the cloth that the swindlers said they could weave?

3. Why was the old minister afraid to tell the truth?

4. Who was the only honest person in the story?

5. How do you think the people felt when they discovered that they had been tricked?

As Rich
As Croesus

James Baldwin

The night has a thousand eyes,
    And the day but one;
Yet the light of the whole world dies
    With the dying sun.

The mind has a thousand eyes,
    And the heart but one;
Yet the light of a whole life dies
    When love is done.
                            —*F. W. Bourdillon*

Some thousands of years ago there lived in Asia a king whose name was Croesus. The country over which he ruled was not very large, but its people were prosperous and famed for their wealth. Croesus himself was said to be the richest man in the world; and so well known is his name that, to this day, it is not uncommon to say of a very wealthy person that he is "as rich as Croesus."

King Croesus had everything that could make him happy—lands and houses and slaves, fine clothing to wear, and beautiful things to look at. He

---

Croesus (krē′səs)—*a fabulously rich Lydian king of the sixth century, B.C.*
prosperous—*rich*

could not think of anything he needed to make him more comfortable or contented. "I am the happiest man in the world," he said.

It happened one summer that a great man from across the sea was traveling in Asia. The name of this man was Solon, and he was the lawmaker of Athens in Greece. He was noted for his wisdom; and, centuries after his death, the highest praise that could be given to a learned man was to say, "He is as wise as Solon."

Solon had heard of Croesus, and so one day he visited him in his beautiful palace. Croesus was now happier and prouder than ever before, for the wisest man in the world was his guest. He led Solon through his palace and showed him the grand rooms, the fine carpets, the soft couches, the rich furniture, the pictures, the books. Then he invited him out to see his gardens and his orchards and his stables; and he showed him thousands of rare and beautiful things that he had collected from all parts of the world.

In the evening as the wisest of men and the richest of men were dining together, the king said to his guest, "Tell me now, O Solon, who do you think is the happiest of all men?" He expected that Solon would say, "Croesus."

Solon (sō′lən)

The wise man
was silent for a minute, and then he
said, "I have in mind a poor man who once lived
in Athens and whose name was Tellus. He, I doubt
not, is the happiest of all men."

This was not the answer that Croesus wanted;
but he hid his disappointment and asked, "Why do
you think so?"

"Because," answered his guest, "Tellus was
an honest man who labored hard for many years

to bring up his children and to give them a good education; and when they were grown and able to do for themselves, he joined the Athenian army and gave his life bravely in the defense of his country. Can you think of anyone who is more deserving of happiness?"

"Perhaps not," answered Croesus, half choking with disappointment. "But who do you think ranks next to Tellus in happiness?" He was quite sure now that Solon would say "Croesus."

"I have in mind," said Solon, "two young men whom I knew in Greece. Their father died when they were mere children, and they were very poor. But they worked manfully to keep the house together and to support their mother, who was in feeble health. Year after year they toiled, nor thought of anything but their mother's comfort. When at length she died they gave all their love to Athens, their native city, and nobly served her as long as they lived."

Then Croesus was angry. "Why is it," he asked, "that you make me of no account and think that my wealth and power are nothing? Why is it that you place these poor working people above the richest king in the world?"

"O king," said Solon, "no man can say whether you are happy or not until you die. For no man

knows what misfortunes may overtake you, or
what misery may be yours in place of all this splendor."

Many years after this there arose in Asia a powerful king whose name was Cyrus. At the head of a
great army he marched from one country to another,
overthrowing many a kingdom and attaching it to
his great empire of Babylon. King Croesus with all
his wealth was not able to stand against this mighty

Cyrus (sī′rəs)

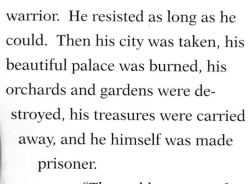

warrior. He resisted as long as he could. Then his city was taken, his beautiful palace was burned, his orchards and gardens were destroyed, his treasures were carried away, and he himself was made prisoner.

"The stubbornness of this man Croesus," said King Cyrus, "has caused us much trouble and the loss of many good soldiers. Take him and make an example of him for other petty kings who may dare to stand in our way."

Thereupon the soldiers seized Croesus and dragged him to the marketplace, handling him roughly all the time. Then they built up a great pile of dry sticks and timber taken from the ruins of his once beautiful palace. When this was finished, they tied the unhappy king in the midst of it, and one ran for a torch to set it on fire.

"Now we shall have a merry blaze," said the savage fellows. "What good can all his wealth do him now?"

_____
petty—*unimportant*

As poor Croesus, bruised and bleeding, lay upon the pyre without a friend to soothe his misery, he thought of the words which Solon had spoken to him years before: "No man can say whether you are happy or not until you die," and he moaned, "O Solon! O Solon! Solon!"

It so happened that Cyrus was riding by at that very moment and heard his moans. "What does he say?" he asked of the soldiers.

"He says, 'Solon, Solon, Solon!'" answered one.

Then the king rode nearer and asked Croesus, "Why do you call on the name of Solon?"

Croesus was silent at first; but after Cyrus had repeated his question kindly, he told all about Solon's visit at his palace and what he had said.

The story affected Cyrus deeply. He thought of the words, "No man knows what misfortunes may overtake you, or what misery may be yours in place of all this splendor." And he wondered if sometime he, too, would lose all his power and be helpless in the hands of his enemies.

"After all," said he, "ought not men to be merciful and kind to those who are in distress? I will do to Croesus as I would have others do to me." And he caused Croesus to be given his freedom;

---

pyre—*a fire*

and ever afterwards treated him as one of his most
honored friends.

Character Theme—Kindness & Wisdom

Thinking It Through

1. What does the statement "rich as Croesus"
   mean?

2. Is true happiness found in wealth? Where is
   it found?

3. What men were truly happy? Why?

4. What changed King Cyrus's mind about Croesus?

Nests

Make yourselves nests of pleasant thoughts! None of us yet know, for none of us have been taught in early youth, what fairy palaces we may build of beautiful thoughts, proof against all adversity; bright fancies, satisfied memories, noble histories, faithful sayings, treasure-houses of precious and restful thoughts, which care cannot disturb, nor pain make gloomy, nor poverty take away from us; houses built without hands, for our souls to live in.

—*John Ruskin*

adversity—*trials or hardship*

The Blind Men & the Elephant

It was six men of Indostan,
   To learning much inclined,
Who went to see the elephant
   (Though all of them were blind),
That each by observation
   Might satisfy his mind.

The first approached the elephant,
   And, happening to fall
Against his broad and sturdy side,
   At once began to bawl:
"Why, bless me! but the elephant
   Is very like a wall!"

---

bawl—*shout*

The second feeling of the tusk,
  Cried: "Ho! what have we here,
So very round, and smooth, and sharp?
  To me 'tis very clear,
This wonder of an elephant
  Is very like a spear!"

The third approached the animal,
  And, happening to take
The squirming trunk within his hands,
  Thus boldly up he spake:
"I see," quoth he, "the elephant
  Is very like a snake!"

The fourth reached out his eager hand,
  And felt about the knee:
"What most this wondrous beast is like,
  Is very plain," quoth he:
" 'Tis clear enough the elephant
  Is very like a tree!"

The fifth, who chanced to touch the ear,
  Said: "E'en the blindest man
Can tell what this resembles most;
  Deny the fact who can,
This marvel of an elephant
  Is very like a fan!"

The sixth no sooner had begun
　　About the beast to grope,
Than, seizing on the swinging tail
　　That fell within his scope,
"I see," quoth he, "the elephant
　　Is very like a rope!"

And so these men of Indostan
　　Disputed loud and long,
Each in his own opinion
　　Exceeding stiff and strong;
Though each was partly in the right,
　　And all were in the wrong.

—*John G. Saxe*

disputed—*argued*

The First Printer

James Baldwin (adapted)

One evening in midsummer, nearly six hundred years ago, a stranger arrived in the old town of Haarlem, in the Netherlands. The people eyed him curiously as he trudged down the main street, and there were many guesses as to who he might be. A traveler in those days was a rarity in Haarlem—a thing to be looked at and talked about. This traveler was dressed poorly and had neither servant nor horse. He carried his knapsack on his shoulder and was covered with dust, as though he had walked far.

He stopped at a little inn close by the market-place and asked for lodging. The landlord was pleased with his looks. He was a young man, bright of eye and quick of movement.

"My name," he said, "is John Gutenberg, and my home is in Mainz."

"Ah, in Mainz, is it?" exclaimed the landlord.

Haarlem (här′ləm)
rarity—*something that rarely happens*

Gutenberg (go͞ot′′n·bûrg)
Mainz (mīnts)

"And why, pray, do you leave Germany and come to our good Haarlem?"

"I am a traveler," answered Gutenberg.

"A traveler! And why do you travel?" inquired the landlord.

"I am traveling to learn," was the answer. "I am trying to gain knowledge by seeing the world. I have been to Genoa and Venice and Rome."

"Ah, have you been so far? Surely, you must have seen great things," said the landlord.

"Yes," said Gutenberg; "I have walked through Switzerland and Germany, and now I am on my way to France."

"How wonderful!" exclaimed the landlord. "And now, while your supper is being cooked, pray tell me what is the strangest thing you have seen while traveling."

"The strangest thing? Well, I have seen towering mountains and the great sea; I have seen savage beasts and famous men; but nowhere have I seen anything stranger than the ignorance of the common people. They know nothing about the country in which they live; and they have scarcely heard of other lands. The saddest thing of all is that they do not have God's Word. It takes so long to copy the

---

Genoa, Venice, Rome—*cities in Italy*
savage—*fierce; untamed*

Bible by hand that it is locked up in the churches and monasteries. The people need to have God's Word and be taught to read it."

"I guess you are right," said the landlord; "but what difference does it make?"

"It makes a great difference," answered Gutenberg. "So long as the common people are ignorant of the Bible, they have to depend on others to tell them what is true. Now, if there were only some way to make books plentiful and cheap, the poorest man might learn to read and thus gain knowledge of what the Bible really says. But as things are, it is only the rich who can buy books. Every volume must be written carefully by hand, and the cost of making it is greater than the earnings of any common man for a lifetime."

"Well," said the landlord, "we have a man here in Haarlem who makes books. He calls it *printing,* I think."

"Who is this man? Tell me where I can find him," cried Gutenberg, now much excited.

"His name is Laurence—Laurence Coster," answered the landlord.

"Where does he live? Can I see him?"

"Why, the big house that you see just across the

---

monasteries—*places where monks live and work*
volume—*a book*

marketplace is his. You can find him at home at any time; for since he got into this strange business of making books, he never goes out."

The young traveler lost no time in making the acquaintance of Laurence Coster. The old man was delighted to meet with one who was interested in his work. He showed him the books he had printed. He showed him the types and the little press that he used. The types were made of pieces

making the acquaintance—*getting to know; meeting*

of wood that Coster had whittled out with his pocket-knife.

"It took a long time to make them," he said; "but watch me print a page with them."

He placed a small sheet of paper upon some types which had been properly arranged. With great care he adjusted them all in his press. Then he threw the weight of his body upon a long lever that operated the crude machine.

"See now the printed page," he cried, as he carefully drew the sheet out.

Gutenberg was delighted.

"It was by accident that I discovered it," said old Laurence. "I went out into the woods one afternoon with my grandchildren. There were some beech trees there, and the little fellows wanted me to carve their names on the smooth bark. I did so, for I was always handy with a pocketknife. Then, while they were running around, I split off some fine pieces of bark and cut the letters of the alphabet upon them—one letter on each piece. I thought they would amuse the youngest grandchild, and perhaps help him to remember his letters. So I wrapped them in a piece of soft paper and carried them home. When I unwrapped the package, I was surprised to see the forms of some of the letters distinctly printed on the white paper. It set me to thinking, and at last I thought out this whole plan of printing books."

"And a great plan it is!" cried Gutenberg. "Ever since I was a boy at school I have been trying to invent some such thing."

He asked Laurence Coster a thousand questions, and the old man kindly told him all that he knew.

"Now, indeed, knowledge will fly to the ends of the earth," said the delighted young traveler as he hastened back to his inn. He could scarcely wait to be gone.

The next morning he was off for Mainz.

At Mainz young Gutenberg shut himself up in a hired room and began to make sets of type like those which Laurence Coster had shown him. He arranged them in words and sentences. He experimented with them until he was able to print much faster than old Laurence had done.

Finally, he tried types of soft metal and found them better than those of wood. He learned to mix ink so it would not spread when pressed by the type. He made brushes and rollers for applying it evenly and smoothly. He improved this thing and that, until at last he was able to do that which he had so long desired—make a book so quickly and cheaply that even a poor man could afford to buy it.

And thus the art of printing by movable type— the most important invention in the world—was discovered. The first and most important book that Gutenberg printed was the Bible. Before long,

people all over northern Europe were reading God's
Word and having their lives changed by it. When
the Pilgrims and Puritans came to America in the
1600s, they brought with them copies of the Bible
in their own English language. They made sure that
their children learned to read the Bible, to love it,
and to obey it. Thus a German inventor in the 1400s
whose dream was to make the Bible available to the
common people helped pave the way for our country
to be founded on the truths of God's Word.

Character Theme—Aspirations, Initiative,
& Resourcefulness

Thinking It Through

1. What country did John Gutenberg come from?

2. Why was Gutenberg traveling?

3. What was the saddest thing that Gutenberg had learned while traveling?

4. Why didn't the common people have Bibles?

5. How did Coster discover how to make type?

6. What was the first book that John Gutenberg printed?

Books

A travel book's a good ship
  With sail unfurled.
We go aboard with willing hearts
  And sail around the world,—
To this port and that port,
  To lands new and old,
And sail back when journey's done
  With treasure in our hold.

A storybook's a castle;
  It has a secret stair.
From room to room we wander,
  And every one is fair.
A lesson book's a meadow
  Where grain is planted deep,
A rich and golden harvest
  That anyone may reap.

A poetry book's a garden
    With lovely gate set wide,
With shady walks, and fountains,
    And flowers on every side.
You pluck a violet,
    I take a rose—
They last through the long years,
    As everybody knows.

This book and that book—
    We're richer than a mint.
Blessings on the good men
    Who first learned to print!

        —*Nancy Byrd Turner*

----

mint—*a place where money is made*

The Last Lesson

Alphonse Daudet

God grants liberty only to those
who love it and are always ready to
defend it.
　　　　　　　　—Daniel Webster

Franz didn't want to go to school that
morning. He would much rather have
played outside. The air was so warm and still, he
could hear the blackbird singing at the edge of the
wood. Now he could hear the sound of the Prussian
soldiers drilling down in the meadow behind the old
sawmill. Then he remembered—this was the day for
the lesson in the rule of participles in French class,
and Franz did not know it at all. All he knew was
that he did not want to go to school.

But, somehow, he went. His legs carried him re-
luctantly into the village and along the street. As he
passed the official bulletin board in front of the town
hall, he noticed a little crowd around it, looking at it.
That was the place where the Prussians posted the
news of lost battles and the demands for new taxes.

Prussia—*the German state that was trying to take over France*
participle—*a special kind of word. The rule of participles is very
long and difficult in the French language.*

88

"What *now*, I wonder?" But he could not stop to see; he was afraid of being late.

When he came to the schoolyard, his heart beat very fast. He was afraid he *was* late, for the windows were all open and yet he heard no noise—the school-room was perfectly quiet. He had been counting on the noise and confusion before school to let him slip quietly into his seat unnoticed. But no; he had to open the door and walk up the long aisle in the midst of a silent room, with the teacher looking straight at him. Oh, how hot his cheeks felt, and how hard his heart beat!

To his great surprise, the teacher didn't scold at all. All he said was, "Come quickly to your place, my little Franz; we were just going to begin without you!"

Franz could hardly believe his ears; that wasn't at all the way the teacher usually spoke to someone who was late. It was very strange! Somehow, every-thing was very strange. Everybody was sitting so still, so straight, and the teacher was wearing his best clothes, the ones he saved for Sundays and for very special occasions.

Franz looked all around, wondering. And there in the back of the room was the oddest thing of all. There, on a bench, sat *visitors*. Visitors! It seemed that all the people of the village had come to school that day. The mayor was there, and the old black-smith, and the farmer, all sitting quiet and still.

Just then the teacher stood up and opened school. He said, "My children, this is the last time I shall ever teach you. The order has come from Berlin that henceforth nothing but German shall be taught in the schools of Alsace. This is your last lesson in French. I beg you, be very attentive."

His last lesson in French! Franz could not believe his ears; his last lesson—ah, *that* was what was on the bulletin board! It flashed across him in an instant. That was it! His last lesson in French—and he scarcely knew how to read and write! He looked down at his books, all battered and torn at the corners, and suddenly his books seemed—some-how—like friends. He looked at the teacher, and he seemed different, too—like a very good friend. Just as he was thinking about it, he heard his name called, and he stood up to recite.

It was the rule of participles.

Oh, what wouldn't he have given to be able to say it from beginning to end, exceptions and all, without a blunder! But he could only stand and hang his head; he did not know a word of it.

Then through the hot pounding in his ears he heard the teacher's voice; it was quite gentle; not at

___
henceforth—*from this time on*
Alsace (al'săs)—*a province on the border of France and Germany*

all the scolding voice he expected. It said, "I'm not going to punish you, Franz. Perhaps you are punished enough. And you are not alone in your fault. We all do the same thing—we all put off our tasks till tomorrow. And sometimes tomorrow never comes. That is the way it has been with us. We have been always putting off our education till the morrow; and they have a right, those Prussians, to say to us, 'What! You call yourselves French, and you cannot even read and write the French language? Learn German, then!'"

And then the teacher spoke to them about the French language. He told them how beautiful it was, how clear and musical and reasonable. He said that no people could be hopelessly conquered as long as they kept their language, for the language was the key to open the door of their prison house. And then he said he was going to tell them a little about that beautiful language, and he explained the rule of participles.

And do you know, it was just as simple as A B C! Franz understood every word. It was just the same with the rest of the grammar lesson. I don't know whether Franz listened harder, or whether the master explained better, but it was all quite clear and simple.

It seemed to Franz that the teacher was trying to put the whole French language into their heads in that one hour. It seemed as if he wanted to teach

them all he knew, before he went—to give them all
he had in this last lesson.

From the grammar the teacher went on to the
penmanship lesson. And for this, he had prepared
clean, new slips of paper with these words at the
top:

France: Alsace.
France: Alsace.

All up and down the aisles they hung out from the
desks like little banners, waving:

France: Alsace.
France: Alsace.

And everybody worked with all his might; not a sound could you hear but the scratching of pens as everyone copied, over and over again, "France: Alsace." Even the little ones bent over their up-and-down strokes with their tongues stuck out to help them work.

After the writing came the reading lesson, and the little ones practiced their phonics. Right in the midst of it, Franz heard a curious sound, a big, deep voice mingling with the children's voices. He turned around, and there, on the bench in the back of the room, the old blacksmith sat with a big A B C book open on his knees. It was his voice Franz had heard. He was saying the sounds with the little children— ba, be, bi, bo, bu. His voice sounded so odd with the little voices that Franz guessed he would laugh; then he guessed he wouldn't laugh; he felt—he felt very strange.

So it went on with the lessons; they had them all. And then, suddenly, the town clock struck noon. And at the same time they heard the tramp of the Prussians' feet, coming back from drill.

It was time to close school.

The teacher stood up. He was very pale. Franz had never seen him look so tall. He said:

"My children—my children"—but something choked him; he could not go on. Instead, he turned and went to the blackboard and took up a piece of chalk. And then he wrote, high up, in big white letters, *"Vive la France!"* "Long live France!"

And he made a little sign to them with his head, "That is all; go away."

Vive la France (vēv′lə·fräns′)—*"Long live France"*

Character Theme—Industry

Thinking It Through

1. Why did Franz not want to go to school?

2. What was usually posted on the official bulletin board outside the town hall?

3. Why didn't Franz wait to read what was posted on the bulletin board?

4. In what ways did the atmosphere of his classroom seem strange?

5. Why would no more French be taught?

6. Why did Franz not laugh at the blacksmith as he recited his sounds?

7. How did Franz change in his attitude toward his language?

Ali, the Boy Camel Driver

We need the faith to go a path untrod,
The power to be alone and vote with God.
—Edwin Markham

Hassan was a camel driver, and it was his business to go backward and forward across the desert to Suez, to take care of the camels. He had a son named Ali, about twelve years of age.

One day, when Hassan had been absent three months, his wife received a message from him, saying that he wished her to send Ali and his camel with the next caravan going to Suez. He would stop there till the boy arrived.

Ali was delighted at the thought of crossing the desert with a caravan in charge of his own camel, of which he was very fond. His mother was anxious at the thought of her son taking so long a journey, though she was pleased that Ali should be able to help his father.

The camel was their most valuable possession, and had been bought after many years of self-denial and careful saving. Though it was so big and clumsy

---

Ali (ä′lē)
Hassan (hä·sän′)
Suez (soo·ĕz′)—*seaport in
northeast Egypt*

caravan—*a group of people
traveling together (as
through a desert)*
self-denial—*sacrificing one's
own wishes or desires*

95

in appearance, it was as gentle as a child. Ali called it Meek-eye. At the sound of his voice, the camel would come when it was called, and kneel down while its master mounted or the load was put on its back.

So Ali made ready the trappings of the camel. He saw that the water bottles did not leak, for, as they were made of skin, they were apt to crack. At last, he joined a caravan that was going to Suez. They filled their water bottles at the wells near the gates of the city. Then, having bidden his mother a fond farewell, Ali started off with a light heart.

The leading camels had bells on their necks and were ridden by the guides. All the other camels followed the sound of the bells. So they tramped steadily into the desert, the large spongy feet of the camels making a swishing sound as they pressed into the soft sand, while the drivers laughed and talked as they rode along. No one took notice of Ali, who was the only boy in the party, but he was able to talk to Meek-eye, and so kept up a stout heart.

Toward the middle of the day it became so hot that the sand seemed to be on fire. There was no breeze to cool and refresh them. Nothing was to be seen but sand, rocks, and sky. At noon a halt was called where a small stream gushed out of the rocks. At night the party encamped for rest, the camels lying down while fires were lighted and food was cooked.

For days they journeyed on without accident, but on the fifth day, about noon, the sky became overcast. A wind sprang up, the sand of the desert began to move about, and in a few minutes one of the dreaded sandstorms was upon them. The camels at once lay down and pushed their noses into the sand. Their drivers threw themselves flat upon the earth in the shelter given by the bodies of the camels.

After the storm had passed, a cry of despair was heard from the drivers. The storm had covered the

_____
spongy—*light; soft; like a sponge*

track with sand, and it was impossible to tell which way to go. So they wandered aimlessly. Three days passed thus, and then a graver danger was felt. The water bottles were dry.

That night, as Ali lay beside his camel, he heard one of the drivers say to a chief trader, "There is only one thing to be done. We must kill a camel and get the water in its stomach. We ought to take the boy's camel. Neither he nor his camel will be missed!"

Poor little Ali trembled with fear as he heard these words. What was he to do, alone among these men fierce with thirst? But as he thought of his camel and the father and mother he loved so well, a sudden resolve sprang up within him. He lay quite still till all was hushed in the camp. Then, whispering a few words in his camel's ears, he noiselessly mounted and stole away.

On he went through the silent night, with his faithful camel under him and the silent stars above.

As he went he prayed to the God of his fathers to
bring him safely through the desert. At last day
broke, and Ali saw all around him nothing but the
vast expanse of sand. Toward noon he became so
faint with thirst that he nearly dropped off his camel.
He felt that very soon there would be nothing left to
do but to lie down and die.

Just then the camel plunged forward a little
faster. Straining his eyes, Ali saw in the far dis-
tance the top of a palm tree. But the camel had
seen it first, and was now hastening on. In a short
time both were having a long drink from a well,

which gave trees and fertility to a small oasis in the desert.

After a refreshing sleep Ali awoke, and now noticed the marks of recent steps upon the sand. He knew that a caravan had been there just before him. He pushed on as fast as he could, and shortly after dusk he saw the welcome blaze of campfires. Soon he found himself one of a circle of camel drivers, who gave him food and drink and listened to his tale.

Happy were Ali's dreams, now that he felt his troubles were nearly over. He was awakened by the shouts of drivers and the tinkling of camel bells from a new party, which had just reached the wells. As he lay listening in a sleepy fashion to these new sounds, he heard a voice that made him jump from the ground. Could he be mistaken? No, it was the sound of his father's voice, and in an instant he was in his father's arms.

Hassan had waited at Suez for some time, but as Ali did not come he thought that there had been some mistake, and started for home. What a joyful meeting there was a few days later, when Ali told his tale to his mother, who lifted up her heart in thankfulness to the great Father, who had brought her son safely home to her through so many dangers.

Character Theme—Adventure, Faith, & Family

Thinking It Through

1. Why was Ali excited about going out to meet his father?

2. When the caravan was lost and thirsty, what did they decide to do?

3. Why did Ali leave the caravan and go on alone? Was he thinking only of himself?

4. What did Ali pray for as he traveled through the night?

5. What did Ali's mother do when she heard about Ali's adventures?

The Arrow & the Song

I shot an arrow into the air;
It fell to earth, I knew not where;
For, so swiftly it flew, the sight
Could not follow it in its flight.

I breathed a song into the air;
It fell to earth, I knew not where;
For who has sight so keen and strong,
That it can follow the flight of song?

Long, long afterward, in an oak,
I found the arrow, still unbroke;
And the song, from beginning to end,
I found again in the heart of a friend.

—*Henry W. Longfellow*

Three  Questions *Leo Tolstoy*

One gentle word that we may speak,
Or one kind, loving deed,
May, though a trifle, poor and weak,
Prove like a tiny seed;
And who can tell what good may spring
From such a very little thing?

It once occurred to a certain king that if he always knew the right time to begin anything, if he knew who were the right people to listen to and whom to avoid—and, above all, if he always knew what was the most important thing to do—he would never fail in an undertaking.

So he had it proclaimed throughout his kingdom that he would give a great reward to anyone who would teach him what was the right time for every action, who were the most necessary people, and what was the most important thing to do.

Many learned men came to the king, but they all answered his questions differently.

All the answers being different, the king agreed with none of the scholars and gave the reward to none. But still wishing to find the right answer to his questions, he decided to consult a hermit widely known for his wisdom.

The hermit lived in a wood which he never left, and he received none but humble folk. So the king put on simple clothes; then before reaching the hermit's cell he dismounted from his horse, and leaving his bodyguard behind, went on alone.

When the king approached, the hermit was digging the ground in front of his hut. Seeing the king, he greeted him and went on digging. The hermit was frail and weak, and each time he stuck his spade into the ground and turned a little earth, he breathed heavily.

The king went up to him and said, "I have come to you, wise hermit, to ask you to answer three questions: How can I learn to do the right thing at the right time? Who are the people who can help me most? What affairs are the most important and need my first attention?"

The hermit listened to the king, but answered nothing. He just spat on his hand and went on digging.

"You are tired," said the king. "Let me take the spade and work a while for you."

"Thank you!" said the hermit, and giving the spade to the king, he sat down on the ground.

---

hermit—*a person who lives by himself in a lonely spot*
dismount—*to get off (a horse, bicycle, etc.)*
frail—*slender and delicate*

When he had dug two beds, the king stopped
and repeated his questions. The hermit again gave
no answer, but rose, stretched out his hand for the
spade, and said, "Now rest a while—and let me work
a bit." But the king did not give him the spade, and
continued to dig. One hour passed and another.
The sun began to sink behind the trees, and the king
at last stuck the spade into the ground and said, "I
came to you, wise man, for an answer to my questions. If you can give me none, tell me so, and I will
return home."

"Here comes someone running," said the hermit.
"Let us see who it is."

The king turned around and saw a bearded man
come hurrying out of the wood.
The man held his hands
pressed against his breast,
and blood was flowing
from under them.
When he reached
the king, he fell
fainting on
the ground,
moaning
feebly. The
king and
the hermit

unfastened the man's clothing. There was a large wound in his body. The king washed it as best he could, and bandaged it with his handkerchief and with a towel the hermit found. But the blood would not stop flowing, and the king again and again washed and rebandaged the wound.

When at last the blood had ceased flowing, the man revived and asked for something to drink. The king brought fresh water and gave it to him. Meanwhile the sun had set, and it was growing cool. So the king, with the hermit's help, carried the wounded man into the hut and laid him on a bed. The man closed his eyes and was quiet; and the king was so tired with his walk and with the work he had done that he crouched down on the threshold, and also fell asleep—so soundly that he slept all through the short summer night. On awaking in the morning, it was long before he could remember where he was, or who was the strange bearded man lying on the bed and gazing intently at him with shining eyes.

"Forgive me!" said the bearded man in a weak voice, when he saw that the king was awake and looking at him.

"I do not know you, and have nothing to forgive you," said the king.

---

revive—*to come back to consciousness*
crouch—*to stoop low with the knees bent*
threshold—*a piece of wood used at the bottom of a doorway*

"You do not know me, but I know you. I am that enemy of yours who swore to revenge himself on you, because you executed his brother and seized his property. I knew you had gone alone to see the hermit, and I resolved to kill you on your way back. But the day passed and you did not return. So I came out from my ambush to find you, and ran across your bodyguard, who recognized me and wounded me. I escaped from him, but I should have bled to death had you not dressed my wound. I wished to kill you, and you have saved my life. Now, if I live, and if you wish it, I will serve you as your most faithful slave, and will bid my sons do the same. Forgive me!"

The king was very glad to have made peace with his enemy so easily, and to have gained him for a friend; and he not only forgave him, but said that he would send his servants and his own physician to attend him. In the end he promised to restore the man's property.

Having taken leave of the wounded man, the king went out into the porch and looked around for the hermit. Before departing he wished once more to beg an answer to the questions he had put. The hermit was outside, on his knees, sowing seeds in the beds that had been dug the day before.

---

revenge—*to get back at someone*
execute—*to put to death according to a legal order*

resolve—*to determine*
ambush—*a hiding place*

The king approached him and said, "For the last time, I pray you to answer my questions, wise man."

"You have already been answered," said the hermit, still crouching on his thin legs, and looking up at the king, who stood before him.

"How answered? What do you mean?" asked the king.

"Do you not see?" replied the hermit. "If you had not pitied my weakness yesterday and had not dug these beds for me, but had gone your way, that man would have attacked you, and you would have repented leaving me. So the most important time was when you dug the beds; and I was the most important man; and to do me good was your most important business. Afterwards, when that man ran to us, the most important

repent—*to be sorry for*

time was when you attended him, for if you had not bound up his wounds he would have died without making his peace with you. So he was the most important man, and what you did for him was your most important business.

"Remember then: there is only one time that is important—now! It is the truly important time, because it is the only time when we have any power. The most necessary man is he with whom we are, for no one knows whether he will ever have dealings with any other man. And the most important affair is to do him good, because for that purpose alone was man sent into this life!"

Character Theme—Kindness, Service, & Wisdom

Thinking It Through

1. What three things did the king want to learn?

2. After listening to many learned men, whom did the king seek for an answer to his questions?

3. How did the king find the answer to his questions?

4. What has this story taught you about your actions toward those around you?

The
Best That
I Can

I cannot do much," said a little star,
"To make the dark world bright;
My silvery beam cannot struggle far
Through the folding gloom of night;
But I am a part of God's great plan,
And I'll cheerfully do the best I can."

"What is the use," said a fleecy cloud,
"Of these few drops that I hold?
They will hardly bend the lily proud,
Though caught in her cup of gold;
Yet I am a part of God's great plan,
So my treasure I'll give as well as I can."

A child went merrily forth to play,
But a thought, like a silver thread,
Kept winding in and out all day
Through the happy golden head;
And it seemed to say, "Do all you can,
For you are a part of God's great plan."

She knew no more than the glancing star,
  Nor the cloud with its chalice full,
How, why, and for what all strange things are—
  She was only a child at school;
But she thought, "It is a part of God's great plan
  That even I should do all that I can."

So she helped a younger child along,
  When the road was rough to the feet;
And she sang from her heart a little song
  That we all thought was passing sweet;
And her father, a weary, toil-worn man,
  Said, "I, too, will do the best that I can."

---

chalice—*a cup or goblet*

Dr. Johnson
and His Father

James Baldwin

It is in a little bookshop in the city of Lichfield, England. The floor has just been swept and the shutter taken down from the one small window. The hour is early, and customers have not yet begun to drop in. Out of doors the rain is falling.

At a small table near the door, a feeble, white-haired old man is making up some packages of books. As he arranges them in a large basket, he stops now and then as though disturbed by pain. He puts his hand to his side; he coughs in a most distressing way; then he sits down and rests himself, leaning his elbows upon the table.

"Samuel!" he calls.

In the farther corner of the room there is a young man busily reading from a large book that is spread open before him. He is a very odd-looking fellow, perhaps eighteen years of age, but you would take him to be older. He is large and awkward, with a great round face, scarred and marked by a strange

---

Lichfield (lĭch′fĕld)

disease. His eyesight must be poor, for, as he reads, he bends down until his face is quite near the printed page.

"Samuel!" again the old man calls.

But Samuel makes no reply. He is so deeply interested in his book that he does not hear. The old man rests himself a little longer and then finishes tying his packages. He lifts the heavy basket and sets it on the table. The exertion brings on another fit of coughing; and when it is over he calls for the third time, "Samuel!"

"What is it, Father?" This time the call is heard.

"You know, Samuel," he says, "that tomorrow is market day at Uttoxeter, and our stall must be attended to. Some of our friends will be there to look at the new books which they expect me to bring. One of us must go down on the stage this morning and get everything in readiness. But I hardly feel able for the journey. My cough troubles me quite a little, and you see that it is raining very hard."

"Yes, Father; I am sorry," answers Samuel, and his face is again bent over the book.

"I thought perhaps you would go down to the market, and that I might stay here at the shop," says his father. But Samuel does not hear. He is deep in the study of some Latin classic.

---

exertion—*exercise; work*   **Uttoxeter** (ŭ·tŏk′sə·tər)

The old man goes to the door and looks out. The rain is still falling. He shivers, and buttons his coat.

It is a twenty-mile ride to Uttoxeter. In five minutes the stage will pass the door.

"Samuel, will you not go down to the market for me this time?"

The old man is putting on his great coat.

He is reaching for his hat.

The basket is on his arm.

He casts a beseeching glance at his son, hoping that he will relent at the last moment.

"Here comes the coach, Samuel"; and the old man is choked by another fit of coughing.

Whether Samuel hears or not, I do not know. He is still reading, and he makes no sign nor motion.

The stage comes rattling down the street.

The old man with his basket of books staggers out of the door. The stage halts for a moment while he climbs inside. Then the driver swings his whip, and all are away.

Samuel, in the shop, still bends over his book.

Out of doors the rain is falling.

---

beseech—*to ask earnestly*
relent—*to give in*

⤳ Scene Two ⤳

Just fifty years have passed, and again it is market day at Uttoxeter.

The rain is falling in the streets. The people who have wares to sell huddle under the eaves and in the stalls and booths that have roofs above them.

A carriage from Lichfield pulls up at the entrance to the market square.

An old man alights. One would guess him to be seventy years of age. He is large and not well-shaped. His face is seamed and scarred, and he makes strange grimaces as he clambers out of the carriage. He wheezes and puffs as though afflicted with asthma. He walks with the aid of a heavy stick.

With slow but ponderous strides he enters the market place and looks around. He seems not to know that the rain is falling.

He looks at the little stalls ranged along the walls of the market place. Some have roofs over them and are the centers of noisy trade. Others have fallen into disuse and are empty.

The stranger halts before one of the latter. "Yes, this is it," he says. He has a strange habit of talking

---

eaves—*edges of a roof*
grimace—*a facial expression*

clambers—*climbs with difficulty*
ponderous—*very heavy*

aloud to himself. "I remember it well. It was here that my father, on certain market days, sold books to the clergy of the county. The good men came from every parish to see his wares and to hear him describe their contents."

He turns abruptly around. "Yes, this is the place," he repeats.

He stands quite still and upright, directly in front of the little old stall. He takes off his hat; his great walking stick has fallen into the gutter. He bows his head and clasps

his hands. He does not seem to know that the rain is falling.

The clock in the tower above the market strikes eleven. The passers-by stop and gaze at the stranger. The market people peer at him from their booths and stalls. Some laugh as the rain runs in streams down his scarred old cheeks. Rain is it? Or can it be tears?

Boys hoot at him. Some of the ruder ones even hint at throwing mud; but a sense of shame withholds them from the act.

"He is a poor lunatic. Let him alone," say the more compassionate.

The rain falls upon his bare head and his broad shoulders. He is drenched and chilled. But he stands motionless and silent, looking neither to the right nor to the left.

"Who is that old fool?" asks a thoughtless young man who chances to be passing.

"Do you ask who he is?" answers a gentleman from London. "Why, he is Dr. Samuel Johnson, the most famous man in England. It was he who wrote *Rasselas* and the *Lives of the Poets* and *Irene* and many another work which all men are praising. It was he who made the great English dictionary, the most wonderful book of our times. In London, the noblest lords and ladies take pleasure in doing him honor. He is the literary lion of England."

"Then why does he come to Uttoxeter and stand thus in the pouring rain?"

"I cannot tell you; but doubtless he has reasons for doing so"; and the gentleman passes on.

At length there is a lull in the storm. The birds are chirping among the housetops. The people wonder if the rain is over, and venture out into the slippery street.

The clock in the tower above the market strikes twelve. The renowned stranger has stood a whole hour motionless in the market place. And again the rain is falling.

Slowly now he returns his hat to his head. He finds his walking stick where it had fallen. He lifts his eyes reverently for a moment, and then, with a lordly, lumbering motion, walks down the street to meet the carriage which is ready to return to Lichfield.

We follow him through the pattering rain to his native town.

"Why, Dr. Johnson!" exclaims his hostess. "We have missed you all day. And you are so wet and chilled! Where have you been?"

---

literary—*having to do with writers*   renowned—*famous*
venture—*to do or go at some risk*

"Madam," says the great man, "fifty years ago, this very day, I stubbornly refused to oblige or obey my father. The thought of the pain which I must have caused him has haunted me ever since. To do away the sin of that hour, I this morning went in a carriage to Uttoxeter and did do penance publicly before the stall which my father had formerly used."

The great man bows his head upon his hands and sobs.

Out of doors the rain is falling.

Dr. Samuel Johnson was England's greatest writer in the 1700s. His most famous book was his great dictionary, which he spent eight years re-searching and writing. Before Johnson's dictionary, people invented their own spellings for words, and sometimes a writer would spell a word two or three different ways in the same book. Samuel Johnson's dictionary quickly became the standard for the spelling and meanings of words in both England and the United States.

In Dr. Johnson's day, many English people either laughed at the Bible or ignored it. The great Dr. Johnson, however, believed that every word of the Bible is true. His love for God's Word made him a

---

oblige—*to do a favor for*
penance—*a voluntary suffering to show sorrow for sin*

humble man, and it made him ashamed of the way he had treated his father on that rainy day in his youth.

Character Theme—Family & Kindness

Thinking It Through

1. Did the young boy show concern for his father's ill health?

2. Why did the father have to go to the market? Why should he not have gone?

3. Fifty years after the first incident, did the son still remember how he had dishonored his father? What did he do to ease his guilt?

From the Bible

Honor thy father and thy mother: that thy days may be long upon the land which the LORD thy God giveth thee.

—*Exodus 20:12*

Somebody's *Mother*

Sanford

When our train reached Clinton, the conductor entered the car and, taking the bundles of a very old lady, helped her to the platform. Giving her his arm, he assisted her to the waiting room and placed her bundles beside her. He then signaled the engineer and boarded the moving train. A gentleman interested in the scene said, "I beg pardon, Mr. Conductor, but was that old lady your mother?" "No," said the conductor, "but she was somebody's mother."

Thinking Only of Myself

Hezekiah Butterworth

Once there was a man that thought his whole duty was in serving himself. This he did, and became very poor.

In fact, the more he toiled, the poorer he became. At last he found himself, his wife, and his children without a single cent.

So he went to a wise man to seek his fate. This wise man lived in a forest that was far, far away, and the journey to this forest was rough and dangerous.

In the jungle the poor man met a camel with two sacks of treasure on his back. "Where are you going?" asked the camel.

"To seek my fate," said the man.

"Ask mine, too," said the camel. "I was lost from the caravan, and I have carried these sacks of gold on my back for twelve years. I cannot lie down. Ask mine, too."

---

toil—*to work hard and continuously*

"I will," said the man. And he went on.

Then he came to a wide river in which was a great alligator.

"Take me across," said the man.

"I will," said the alligator. "Where are you going?"

"To seek my fate."

"Ask mine, too. For twelve years I have had a burning pain and cannot rest. Ask mine too."

"I will," said the man. And he went on his way.

As he journeyed, he found a tiger lying in a thicket in great pain. He was surrounded by the treasures of the men he had eaten.

"Where are you going?" asked the tiger.

"To seek my fate."

"Ask mine, also, for I have had this thorn in my foot for twelve years. I cannot rest. Ask mine, also."

"I will," said the man.

At last the man reached the forest where the wise man lived.

"What do you here?" asked the wise old man.

"I seek my fate. I have twelve children, and am very poor."

"Then you must have been living only for yourself. Think only of making others rich, and you will become rich yourself."

---

thicket—*a thick growth of shrubs or underbrush*

Then the man asked the fate of the camel.

"Take the sacks off his back, and both of you will be relieved. Why did you not do it before?"

"I was thinking only of myself, " said the man.

Then he asked the fate of the alligator.

"Give him herbs," said the wise man, "and both of you will be relieved. Why did you not do it before?"

"I was thinking only of myself." Then he asked the fate of the tiger.

"Take the thorn out of his foot, and both of you will be relieved. Why did you not think of that before?"

"I was thinking only of myself," said the man.

Then the man returned to the tiger.

"Have you found my fate?" asked the tiger.

herb (ûrb)—*a plant used as medicine, seasoning, or food*

The man drew the thorn out of the tiger's foot, and started to go on.

"Here, take the treasure," said the tiger. "I did not think of it before." So the man took the treasure, and hastened to the river where he had seen the alligator.

"Have you found my fate?" asked the alligator. "I am burning up."

The man found a few herbs, and gave them to the alligator. They made the alligator sick, and he cast up a ruby.

The man started on.

"Stop!" said the alligator, "and take the ruby. It will make you rich."

The man took the ruby. He came at last to the camel.

"Have you found my fate?" asked the camel.

The man took the two sacks from the camel's back, and started on.

ruby—*a valuable gemstone*

"Stop!" said the camel. "These sacks are full of gold. Take them, and both of us will be happy."

The man took the sacks of gold. By the time that he reached home, he was so rich that it took all his twelve children to help him use his wealth.

This wealth was always used for the good of others, so that the man might not again become poor. And he never again did become poor.

Character Theme—Service & Wisdom

Thinking It Through

1. Why was the man so poor?

2. To whom did he go for advice?

3. What three animals did he meet on his journey?

4. What advice did the wise man give to the poor man? Did he follow the advice?

5. What happened when the man returned home?

The Two Words

One day a harsh word rashly said,
upon an evil journey sped,
and, like a sharp and cruel dart,
it pierced a fond and loving heart;
it turned a friend into a foe,
and everywhere brought pain and woe.

A kind word followed it one day,
sped swiftly on its blessed way;
it healed the wound, it soothed the pain,
and friends of old were friends again;
it made the hate and anger cease,
and everywhere brought joy and peace.

But yet the harsh word left a trace
the kind word could not quite erase;
and, though the heart its love regained,
it bore a scar that long remained.
Friends could forgive, but not forget,
or lose the sense of keen regret.

O, if we would but learn to know
how swift and sure one word can go,
how would we weigh with utmost care
each thought before it sought the air,
and only speak the words that move
like white-winged messengers of love!

Character Theme—Kindness

Ladi

Francis F. Harling/
W. Claire Greiner

Ladi waited beside the locust-bean tree at the edge of the village in Africa. She heard the shouts of excited children as they left their mud homes and raced toward her across the soft, sandy earth. She watched for a moment. Then, turning quickly, she began to climb the tree. Her bare feet clung to the bark and her black eyes hunted for the highest branches.

"Wait for us!" a boy shouted.

"Try and catch me!" Ladi answered as she climbed higher. She stretched for a higher branch—but it was out of reach. She stretched and stretched—and suddenly her feet slipped.

"Help!" Ladi screamed, as she fell to the ground.

Ladi lay motionless. Her arm and shoulder hurt too much to move. When she breathed, it seemed as if everything hurt. Men ran from the village and knelt beside her. They touched her arm.

"Oh-h-h!!" Ladi moaned.

"Her arm is broken," one said. "We will have to take her to the missionary."

Carefully, they bound Ladi's arm with a thick rope. Then they carried her down the long road to the mission.

Ladi had never seen a European before. But she forgot her fear after the lady had set the broken arm and bandaged it gently. *How different she is from our witch doctors,* she thought.

The next morning when the patients gathered for worship, Ladi joined them. One of the songs they sang was strange and beautiful. It kept repeating the words, 'The Light of the World is Jesus.' Then one of the missionaries read from a black Book. What wonderful words they were! Ladi listened carefully. The missionary explained, "It was the Lord Jesus Who said that whoever believes on Him should not abide in darkness."

They were strange words to Ladi. *Who is this Lord Jesus, anyway?* she wondered.

Each day she learned more about Him. Soon she understood that Jesus is God's Son. He came from His heavenly home to bring light to boys, girls, men, and women everywhere—people whose hearts are dark with sin. He died on a cross as punishment for the sins of everyone. Ladi could not understand why One so wonderful would die for her.

European (yŏŏr′ ə·pē′ən)

One day the missionary held up a lantern. "Our lives are like this lantern," she explained. "Just as oil is needed to make the wick burn, so the Holy Spirit of God is needed to give light in our hearts."

Ladi was more puzzled than ever. She knew how dark and sinful her heart was. *But how can I get a light inside?* she wondered.

The missionary continued. "When we believe in the Lord Jesus and invite Him into our hearts, He enters our lives, and His glorious light chases away the darkness. Then His Spirit begins to shine through us. Sometimes, though, the globe on this lantern gets covered with dirt and the light cannot shine through. So, too, if our lives are not clean, the Lord Jesus cannot shine forth. We must keep the globe of our hearts clean and bright."

Ladi thought about all this for several days. Finally one afternoon she talked to the missionary. "There is no light in here," she whispered, pointing to her heart.

"Would you like to have a light there, Ladi?" the missionary asked. "The Lord Jesus will come into your life if you ask Him."

"Not today," Ladi answered, shaking her head vigorously.

One dark evening Ladi walked across the mission compound with the missionary. Suddenly a strange

---

wick—*a string in a lamp used to draw oil to the flame*

fear filled her heart. She grabbed the missionary's hand.

"Do not be afraid," the missionary said, holding the lantern in front of them. "This light will show us the path and protect us from the snakes."

"But what about my heart? It is full of darkness, and I do not know what to do. I am more afraid of that than I am of snakes!"

"Satan wants your heart to be dark, Ladi, so he can trick you and lead you into wrong places. But the Lord Jesus Christ defeated Satan when He died

on the cross and rose again. He can take away that darkness in your heart just as this lantern chases away the darkness around us."

"But how can He take my darkness of sin away?" Ladi asked.

"You must invite Him into your heart. He will never force His way in. He says, 'I am the Light of the world: he that followeth Me shall not walk in darkness, but shall have the Light of life.' (John 8:12) Would you like to ask Him to come in?"

Ladi nodded. And there in the lantern-lighted darkness, she bowed her head and asked the Lord Jesus to forgive her sin. "Thank You for dying for me," she prayed. By faith she became a child of God.

After that things were different. No longer did she say bad words. She stopped lying. She even stopped stealing. The darkness was gone, and Ladi could smile when she listened to the missionary read Ephesians 5:8: "For ye were sometimes darkness, but now are ye light in the Lord." Her darkness had indeed become light!

Many weeks later, Ladi's arm was healed. "Today you go home!" the missionary announced. Ladi was excited. She was eager to see her parents and friends. *But what will they say about Jesus?* she wondered. Walking along the winding trail, she prayed: "Dear Lord Jesus, please help me to be a shining light at home. Help me to tell all my friends how wonderful You are. Amen."

Everyone in the small village wondered why Ladi was different. No longer did she quarrel and fight with the other children. Instead, she was kind and considerate. She looked for things that she could do for others. She helped the women with their babies and their work. Every day she helped the old blind lady by grinding her grain and getting water for her.

One day Ladi invited the boys and girls to her home. There she told them what she knew about the Lord Jesus. She also taught them the songs she had learned. Soon all the children were singing, "The Light of the World is Jesus."

The next day, some of the mothers came to the class, and Ladi told them about her wonderful Friend, Jesus Christ. After listening to Ladi day after day, a few of the mothers placed their trust in the Lord Jesus, the Savior of the world.

There was one person who refused to listen when Ladi spoke of the Lord Jesus. That person was her father. Oh, how Ladi prayed for him! God heard Ladi's prayer, for finally one day her father did listen. Ladi asked, "Do you know what God says in Romans 6:23, Father? He says: 'The wages of sin is death; but the gift of God is eternal life through Jesus Christ our Lord.'"

Her father stared silently at the floor. Ladi watched and waited. Finally he picked up his hoe and hurried off to the fields. Poor Ladi! She wanted more than anything else to win her father for the Savior.

She wiped her tears and began to pray: "Dear Lord Jesus, You can answer prayer. I know You can. My father does not believe in You. But he needs You. Please show him how much he needs You. Amen."

A little later, Ladi heard someone hurrying up the path toward the house. It was her father! Something was wrong. Was he angry? Then she saw tears on his face.

"Father, what is wrong?"

"Ladi! Ladi! My sins. I cannot forget what you said. When I went to work, my heart kept repeating the words, 'The wages of sin is death' . . . 'the wages of sin is death.' Ladi, my sins are so many! What shall I do?"

Ladi reached for her father's hand. "But, Father," she said, "you have forgotten the rest of the verse. It says, 'but the gift of God is eternal life through Jesus Christ our Lord.' It is a gift, Father. He wants you to take it. Believe that He is the Son of God. Believe that He will forgive you. Ask Him to forgive you. Ask Him right now."

"Will He give me life?"

"Yes," Ladi assured him, "He will give you eternal life."

Her father knelt on the mud floor and prayed, "Lord Jesus, I am a wicked sinner and I cannot help myself. I believe You died for me. Please save me and forgive me. Please give me the gift of eternal life."

When Ladi looked into her father's face, she knew that the darkness was gone from his heart. How happy she was! How happy her father was!

Character Theme—Faith & Service

Thinking It Through

1. How did Ladi break her arm?

2. Where did the men from the village take Ladi for help?

3. How did the missionary say that our lives are like a lantern?

4. Why was Ladi afraid?

5. What brought light to Ladi's heart?

6. How could the people of Ladi's village tell that she was different?

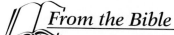

From the Bible

I am the light of the world: he that followeth Me shall not walk in darkness, but shall have the light of life.

—John 8:12

Reflections

T here is dew in one flower and not in another," said Beecher, "because one opens its cup and takes it in, while the other closes itself and drops run off." Are you dissatisfied with today's success? It is the harvest of yesterday's sowing. Do you dream of a golden tomorrow? We get out of life just what we put in it. The world has for us just what we have for it. It is a mirror which reflects the faces we make. If we smile and are glad, it reflects a cheerful sunny face. If we are sour, irritable, mean, and contemptible, it still shows us the true copy of ourselves. The world is a whispering gallery which returns the echo of our voices. What we say of others is said of us. We shall find nothing in the world we do not find first in ourselves.

Billy Topsail's Dog

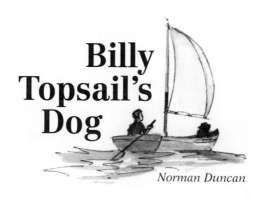

Norman Duncan

~Friendship~

Skipper was a Newfoundland dog who had been brought up in Ruddy Cove. He had black hair—short, straight, and wiry—and broad shoulders. He was heavy, awkward, and ugly, resembling somewhat a great draft horse. But he pulled with a will, and within the knowledge of man had never stolen a fish; so he had a high place in the hearts of all the people of the Cove.

"Skipper! Skipper! Here, boy!"

The ringing call, in the voice of Billy Topsail, never failed to bring the dog from the kitchen with an eager rush, when the snow lay deep on the rocks, and all the paths of the wilderness were ready for the sled. He stood stock-still for the harness, and at the first "Hi, boy! Gee up there!" he bounded away with a wagging tail and a glad bark. It was as if nothing pleased him so much on a frosty morning as the prospect of a hard day's work.

Newfoundland (noo′fənd·lănd′)

If the call came in summertime when Skipper was dozing in the cool shadow of a flake—a platform of boughs for drying fish—he scrambled to his feet and ran full of excitement for what might come, to where young Billy waited. If his collar were taken off, as it was almost sure to be, it meant sport in the water. Then Skipper would paw the ground and whine until the stick was flung out for him. But best of all, he loved to dive for stones.

At the peep of many a day, too, he went out in the punt to the fishing grounds with Billy Topsail, and there kept the lad good company all the day long. It was because he sat up in the bow, as if keeping a lookout ahead, that he was called Skipper.

"Sure, 'tis a clever dog, that!" was Billy's boast. "He would save life—that dog would!"

This was proved beyond doubt when little Isaiah Tommy Goodman toddled over the wharf, where he had been playing. Isaiah Tommy was four years old, and could surely have been drowned had not Skipper strolled down the wharf just at that moment.

Skipper was obedient to the instinct of all Newfoundland dogs to drag the sons of men from water. He plunged in and caught Isaiah Tommy by the collar of his shirt. Still following his instinct, he kept the child's head above water with powerful strokes

---

boughs—*large tree branches*   punt—*a flat-bottomed boat*

140

of his forepaws while he towed him to shore. Then the outcry which Isaiah Tommy immediately set up brought his mother to complete the rescue.

For this deed Skipper was petted for a day and a half, and fed with fried fish and salt pork, to his evident pleasure. No doubt he was persuaded that he had acted worthily. However that be, he continued in merry moods, in affectionate behavior, and in honesty.

One day in the spring of the year, when high winds spring suddenly from the land, Billy Topsail was fishing from his punt, the *Never Give Up*, over the shallows of Molly's Head. It was "fish weather," as the Ruddy Cove men say—gray, cold, and misty. The harbor entrance lay two miles to the southwest. The bluffs which marked it could hardly be seen, for the mist hung thick off the shore. Four punts and a skiff were bobbing half a mile farther out to sea, their crews fishing with hook and line over the sides of the boats. Thicker weather threatened, and the day was nearly over.

" 'Tis time to be off home, boy," said Billy to the dog. " 'Tis getting thick in the sou'west."

Skipper stretched himself and wagged his tail. He had no word to say, but Billy, who, like all fishermen in far-off places, had formed the habit of talking to himself, supplied the answer.

" 'Tis that, Billy, boy," said he. "The punt's as much as one hand can manage in a fair wind. And 'tis a dead beat to the harbor now."

Then Billy said a word for himself. "We'll put in a ballast. The punt's too little for a gale."

He rowed the punt to the little cove by the Head, and there loaded her with rocks. Her sails, mainsail and tiny jib, were spread, and she was pointed for Grassy Island, on the first leg of her beat into the wind. By this time two other punts were under way, and the sails of the skiff were fluttering as her crew prepared to beat home for the night. The *Never Give Up* was ahead of the fleet, and held her lead in such fine fashion as to make Billy Topsail's heart swell with pride.

---

skiff—*a small, light boat*
ballast—*a weight put into a vessel to steady it*

jib—*a triangular sail in front of the mainsail of a boat*

The wind had gained in force. It was sweeping down from the hills in gusts. Now it fell to a breeze, and again it came swiftly with angry strength. Nor could its advance be perceived, for the sea was choppy and the bluffs shielded the inshore waters.

"We'll fetch the harbor on the next tack," Billy muttered to Skipper, who was whining in the bow.

He put the steering oar hard over to bring the punt about. A gust caught the sails. The boat heeled before it, and her gunwale was under water before Billy could make a move to save her. The wind forced her down, pressing heavily upon the canvas.

"Easy!" screamed Billy.

But the ballast of the *Never Give Up* shifted, and she toppled over. Boy and dog were thrown into the sea. Billy dived deep to escape entanglement with the rigging of the boat. He had long ago learned the lesson that the presence of mind wins half the fight in perilous emergencies. The coward miserably perishes where the brave man survives.

With his courage leaping to meet his danger, he struck out and rose to the surface. He looked about for the punt. She had been heavily weighted with

---

perceive—*to be aware of*
gunwale (gŭn′ ′l)—*the upper edge of the side of a boat*

ballast, and he feared for her. What was he to do if she had been too heavily weighted? Even as he looked, she sank. She had righted under water; the tip of the mast was the last he saw of her.

⁓Fear⁓

The sea—cold, fretful, vast—lay all about him. The coast was half a mile away; the punts, out at sea, were laboriously beating toward him, and could make no greater speed. He had to choose between the punts and the rocks.

A whine with a strange note in it attracted Billy's attention. The big dog had caught sight of him, and was beating the water in a frantic effort to approach quickly. But the dog had never whined like that before.

"Hi, Skipper!" Billy called. "Steady, boy! Steady!"

Billy took off his boots as fast as he could. The dog was coming nearer, still whining strangely, and madly pawing the water. Billy was mystified. What possessed the dog? It was as if he had been seized with a fit of terror. Was he afraid of drowning? His eyes were fairly flaring. Such a light had never been in them before.

The boy lifted himself high in the water and looked intently into the dog's eyes. It was terror he saw in them; there could be no doubt about that, he thought. The dog was afraid for his life. At once Billy was filled with dread. He could not crush the feeling down. Afraid of Skipper, the old, affectionate Skipper, his own dog, which he had reared from a puppy! It was absurd.

But he *was* afraid, nevertheless, and he was desperately afraid.

"Back, boy!" he cried. "Get back, sir!"

It chanced that Billy Topsail was a strong swimmer. He had learned to swim where the water is cold, as cold, often, as the icebergs stranded in the harbor can make it. The water was bitter cold now; but he did not fear it; nor did he doubt that he could accomplish the long swim which lay before him. It was the strange behavior of the dog which disturbed

---

mystified—*puzzled; bewildered*
absurd—*making no sense*

him—his failure in obedience, which could not be explained. The dog was now within three yards, and excited past all reason.

"Back, sir!" Billy screamed. "Get back with you!"

Skipper was not held back by the command. He did not so much as hesitate. Billy raised his hand as if to strike him, a threatening gesture which had sent Skipper home with his tail between his legs many a time. But it had no effect now.

"Get back!" Billy screamed again.

It was plain that the dog was not to be bidden. Billy threw himself on his back, supported himself with his hands and kicked at the dog with his feet.

Skipper was blinded by the splashing. He whined and held back. Then blindly he came on again. Billy moved slowly from him, head foremost, still churning the water with his feet. But, swimming thus, he was no match for the dog. With his head thrown back to escape the blows, Skipper forged after him. He was struck in the jaws, in the throat, and again in the jaws. But he pawed on, taking every blow without complaint, and gaining inch by inch. Soon he was so close that the lad could not move his feet freely.

No longer opposed, the dog crept up, paw over paw, forcing the boy's body lower and lower. His object was clear to Billy. Skipper, mad with terror, the boy thought, would try to save himself by climbing on his shoulders.

"Skipper!" he cried. "You'll drown me! Get back!"

The uselessness of attempting to command obedience from a crazy dog struck Billy Topsail with force. He must act otherwise, and that quickly, if he were to escape. There seemed to be but one thing to do. He took a long breath and let himself sink—down, down—as deep as he dared. Down—down—until he retained breath sufficient but to strike to the right and rise again.

The dog, as it was made known later, rose as high as he could force himself, and looked about in every direction, with his mouth open and his ears erect. He gave two sharp barks, like sobs, and a long, mournful whine. Then, as if acting upon a sudden thought, he dived.

For a moment nothing was to be seen of either boy or dog. There was nothing but a choppy sea in that place. Men who were watching thought that both had followed the *Never Give Up* to the bottom.

In the momentary stay under water Billy perceived that his situation was desperate. He would rise, he was sure, but only to renew the struggle. How long he could keep the dog off he could not tell.

Until the punts came down to his aid? He thought
not.

He came to the surface prepared to dive again.
But Skipper had disappeared. An exclamation of
thanksgiving was still on the boy's lips when the
dog's black head rose and moved swiftly toward him.

Billy had a start of about ten yards. He turned
on his side and set off at top speed. There was no
better swimmer among the lads of the harbor. Was
he a match for a powerful Newfoundland dog? It
was soon evident that he was not.

Skipper gained rapidly. Billy felt a paw strike his
foot. He put more strength into his strokes. Next
the paw struck the calf of his leg. The dog was upon
him now, pawing his back. Billy could not sustain
the weight. To escape, that he might take up the
fight in another way, he dived again.

The dog was waiting when Billy came up, waiting eagerly to continue the chase.

"Skipper, old fellow, good old dog!" Billy called in
a soothing voice. "Steady, sir! Down, sir; back!"

The dog was not to be deceived. He came, by
turns whining and gasping. He was more excited,
more determined, than ever. Billy waited for him.
The fight was to be face to face. The boy had determined to keep him off with his hands until strength
failed, to drown him if he could. All love for the dog
had gone out of his heart. The weeks of close and

merry companionship, of romps and rambles and sport, were forgotten; Billy was fighting for life. So he waited without pity, hoping only that his strength might last until he had conquered.

When the dog was within reach, Billy struck him in the face. A snarl and an angry snap were the result.

Rage seemed suddenly to possess the dog. He held back for a moment, growling fiercely, and then attacked with a rush. Billy fought as best he could, trying to clutch his enemy by the neck and to force his head beneath the waves. The effort was vain; the dog eluded his grasp and renewed the attack. In another moment he had laid his heavy paws on the boy's shoulders.

∾Faith∾

The weight was too much for Billy. Down he went, freed himself, and struggled to the surface, gasping for breath. It appeared to him now that he had but a moment to live. He felt his self-possession going from him, and at that moment his ears caught the sound of a voice.

"Put your arm—"

The voice seemed to come from far away. Before the sentence was completed, the dog's paws were again on Billy's shoulders and the water stopped the boy's hearing. What were they calling to him? The

---

elude—*to avoid*

thought that some helping hand was near encouraged him. With this new thought to aid, he dived for the third time. The voice was nearer and clearer when he came up, and he heard every word.

"Put your arm around his neck!" one man cried.

"Catch him by the back of the neck!" cried another.

Billy's self-possession returned. He would follow this direction. Skipper swam anxiously to him. It may be that he wondered what this new attitude meant. It may be that he hoped reason had returned to the boy: that at last he would allow himself to be saved. Billy caught the dog by the back of the neck when he was within arm's length. Skipper wagged his tail and turned about.

There was a brief pause, during which the faithful old dog determined upon the direction he would take. He saw the punts, which had borne down with all speed. Toward them he swam, and there was something of pride in his mighty strokes, something of exultation in his whine. Billy struck out with his free hand, and soon boy and dog were pulled over the side of the nearest punt.

Through it all, as Billy now knew, the dog had only wanted to save him.

Character Theme—Courage, Faithfulness, & Perseverance

Thinking It Through

1. How did Skipper get his name?

2. What is the instinct of all Newfoundland dogs?

3. What did the men of Ruddy Cove say was good fish weather?

4. When the punt turned over, why did Billy dive deep?

5. What wins half the fight in perilous emergencies?

6. In what way did Billy misunderstand Skipper? What was Skipper's feeling toward Billy?

7. What words could be used to describe Skipper?

The Sea

The sea! the sea! the open sea!
The blue, the fresh, the ever free!
Without a mark, without a bound,
It runneth the earth's wide regions round;
It plays with the clouds; it mocks the skies;
Or like a cradled creature lies.

I'm on the sea! I'm on the sea!
I am where I would ever be;
With the blue above, and the blue below,
And silence whersoe'er I go;
If a storm should come and awake the deep,
What matter? I shall ride and sleep.

I love, oh how I love to ride
On the fierce, foaming, bursting tide,
When every mad wave drowns the moon,
Or whistles aloft his tempest tune,
And tells how goeth the world below.
And why the sou'west blasts do blow.

I never was on the dull, tame shore,
But I loved the great sea more and more,
And backward flew to her billowy breast,
Like a bird that seeketh its mother's nest;
And a mother she was, and is, to me;
For I was born on the open sea!

The waves were white, and red the morn,
In the noisy hour when I was born;
And the whale it whistled, the porpoise rolled,
And the dolphins bared their backs of gold;
And never was heard such an outcry wild
As welcomed to life the ocean-child!

I've lived since then, in calm and strife,
Full fifty summers, a sailor's life,
With wealth to spend, and power to range,
But never have sought nor sighed for change;
And Death, whenever he comes to me,
Shall come on the wild, unbounded sea!

—*Barry Cornwall*

billowy—*having large waves*

The Little
Match Girl

Hans Christian Andersen

It was late on a bitterly cold New Year's Eve. The snow was falling. A poor little girl was wandering in the dark cold streets; she was bareheaded and barefoot. She had of course had slippers on when she left home, but they were not much good, for they were so huge. They had last been worn by her mother, and they fell off the poor little girl's feet when she was running across the street to avoid two carriages that were rolling rapidly by. One of the shoes could not be found at all, and the other was picked up by a boy who ran off with it, saying that it would do for a cradle when he had children of his own.

So the poor little girl had to walk on with her little bare feet, which were red and blue with the cold. She carried a quantity of matches in her old apron, and held a packet of them in her hand. Nobody had bought any of her matches during all the long day, and nobody had even given her a copper. The poor little creature was hungry and perishing with cold, and she looked the picture of misery.

---

copper—*a coin like a penny*

154

The snowflakes fell on her long yellow hair, which curled so prettily round her face, but she paid no attention to that. Lights were shining from every window, and there was a most delicious odor of roast goose in the streets, for it was New Year's Eve. She could not forget that! She found a corner where one house projected a little beyond the next one, and here she crouched, drawing up her feet under her, but she was colder than ever. She did not dare to go home, for she had not sold any matches and had not earned a single penny. Her father would beat her, and besides it was almost as cold at home as it was here. They had only the roof over them, and the wind whistled through it although they stuffed up the biggest cracks with rags and straw.

Her little hands were almost stiff with cold. Oh, one little match would do some good! If she only dared, she would pull one out of the packet and strike it on the wall to warm her fingers. She pulled out one. R-r-sh-sh! How it sputtered and blazed! It burnt with a bright clear flame, just like a little candle, when she held her hand round it. Now the light seemed very strange to her! The little girl fancied that she was sitting in front of a big stove with polished brass feet and handles. There was a splendid fire blazing in it and warming her so beautifully,

project—*to stick out*   fancy—*to imagine*

but—what happened? Just as she was stretching out her feet to warm them, the flame went out, the stove vanished—and she was left sitting with the end of the burnt match in her hand.

She struck a new one. It burnt, it blazed up, and where the light fell upon the wall, it became transparent like gauze, and she could see right through it into the room. The table was spread with a snowy cloth and pretty china. A roast goose stuffed with apples and prunes was steaming on it. And what

transparent—*capable of being seen through*
gauze—*any very thin, transparent, loosely woven material*

was even better, the goose hopped from the dish with the carving knife sticking in his back and waddled across the floor. It came right up to the poor child, and then—the match went out, and there was nothing to be seen but the thick black wall.

She lit another match. This time she was sitting under a lovely Christmas tree. It was much bigger and more beautifully decorated than the one she had seen when she peeped through the glass doors at the rich merchant's house this very Christmas. Thousands of lighted candles gleamed under its branches. And many colored pictures, such as she had seen in the shop windows, looked down at her. The little girl stretched out both her hands toward them—then out went the match. All the Christmas candles rose higher and higher, till she saw that they were only the twinkling stars. One of them fell and made a bright streak of light across the sky.

"Someone is dying," thought the little girl, for her old grandmother, the only person who had ever been kind to her, used to say, "When a star falls, a soul is going up to God."

Now she struck another match against the wall, and this time it was her grandmother who appeared in the circle of flame. She saw her quite clearly and distinctly, looking so gentle and happy.

"Grandmother!" cried the little creature. "Oh, do take me with you. I know you will vanish when

the match goes out. You will vanish like the warm
stove, the delicious goose, and the beautiful Christmas tree!"

She hastily struck a whole bundle of matches,
because she did so long to keep her grandmother
with her. The light of the matches made it as bright
as day. Grandmother had never before looked so
big or so beautiful. She lifted the little girl up in her
arms, and they soared in a halo of light and joy, far,
far above the earth, where there was no more cold,
no hunger, and no pain—for they were with God.

---

soar—*to fly high into the air*

In the cold morning light the poor little girl sat there, in the corner between the houses, with rosy cheeks and a smile on her face—dead. Frozen to death on the last night of the old year. New Year's Day broke on the little body still sitting with the ends of the burnt-out matches in her hand.

"She must have tried to warm herself," they said. Nobody knew what beautiful visions she had seen, nor in what a halo she had entered with her grandmother upon the glories of the New Year.

Character Theme—Resourcefulness

Thinking It Through

1. What things in the story tell you that the girl was very poor? What did the girl do to earn money for her father?

2. What things did the girl seem to see when she lit the matches?

3. What happened to the little girl?

The Wind & the Moon

Said the Wind to the Moon, "I will blow you out.
  You stare in the air
  Like a ghost in a chair,
Always looking what I am about.
I hate to be watched; I will blow you out."

The Wind blew hard, and out went the Moon.
  So, deep on a heap
  Of clouds to sleep
Down lay the Wind, and slumbered soon,
Muttering low, "I've done for that Moon."

He turned in his bed; she was there again.
  On high in the sky,
  With her one ghost eye,
The Moon shone white and alive and plain.
Said the Wind, "I will blow you out again."

The Wind blew hard, and the Moon grew dim.
   "With my sledge and my wedge
   I have knocked off her edge.
If only I blow right fierce and grim,
The creature will soon be dimmer than dim."

He blew and he blew, and she thinned to a thread;
   "One puff more's enough
   To blow her to snuff!
One good puff more where the last was bred,
And glimmer, glimmer glum, will go the thread."

He blew a great blast, and the thread was gone;
   In the air nowhere
   Was a moonbeam bare;
Far off and harmless the shy stars shone;
Sure and certain the Moon was gone!

The Wind he took to his revels once more;
   On down, in town,
   Like a merry mad clown,
He leaped and hallooed with whistle and roar.
"What's that?" The glimmering thread once more.

---

sledge—*a large hammer*
revels—*celebrations*

He flew in a rage—he danced and blew;
> But in vain was the pain
> Of his bursting brain;
For still the broader the moon-scrap grew,
The broader he swelled his big cheeks and blew.

Slowly she grew, till she filled the night,
> And shone on her throne
> In the sky alone,
A matchless, wonderful, silvery light,
Radiant and lovely, the queen of the night.

Said the Wind, "What a marvel of power am I!
> With my breath, good faith,
> I blew her to death;—
First blew her away, right out of the sky,
Then blew her in; what a strength am I!"

But the Moon, she knew nothing about the affair,
> For high in the sky,
> With her one white eye,
Motionless, miles above the air,
She had never heard the great Wind blare.

—George MacDonald

Character Theme—Humility

The Birthday

Margaret E. Sangster (adapted)

The boy sat quite alone on the hilltop, his shepherd's crook across his knees, his small square lunch basket beside him. He made an odd shadow in the white light of the moon, for even the fringed shawl that his mother had woven of lamb's wool could not hide the ugly hump that lay between his shoulders.

Far below him, dotting the hillside with other irregular shadows, were the sheep. The majority of them slept, but a few wandered aimlessly up and down the slope. The boy, however, was not watching the flock. His head was thrown back, and his wide eyes were fixed on the sky.

"Perhaps it will happen again," he was thinking, "perhaps—though a third of a century has gone by. Perhaps I shall see the great star and hear the angel voices as my father did!"

The moon, riding high in the heavens, went under a blanket of cloud. For a moment the world was dark. The boy sighed and lowered his eyes.

How often he had listened to the story of the miracle that had taken place so long ago! The boy's father had been a lad himself then—he had been the youngest of the shepherds on that glorious occasion when an angel anthem sounded across the world and a star shone above the tranquil town of Bethlehem. The boy's father had followed the star; with the other shepherds he had come to the stable of the inn. Crowding through the narrow doorway, he had seen a woman with a baby in her arms.

"But—" the boy's father had told the story so many times that his family and the neighbors knew it word for word—"She was no ordinary woman! There was a tenderness in her smile that the very cattle felt. It was not her beauty, although beauty she did possess! It was a shine from within—"

"And the baby—" the boy always prompted his father here—*"what of the baby?"*

"The baby was as unlike other infants as his mother was different from other women. Scarce an hour old when first I glimpsed him, there was a sense of wisdom—no, do not laugh—on his brow, and his tiny up-curled hands seemed—indeed, I do mean it!—to hold power. I found myself kneeling, as the cattle knelt, and there was the damp of tears

---

anthem—*song of praise or devotion*
tranquil—*peaceful*

upon my face, and—though I was a lad tall for my age—I was not ashamed."

Alone on the hillside the boy could almost hear the sound of his father's voice in the stillness. His father's voice telling the story of the marvelous infant and of the Wise Men who had come later—following, also, in the path of the star. They had come bearing gifts, the fame of which traveled through all the land. Often the boy had heard of the gold and frankincense and myrrh; often he had shivered at the tale of the great cruel king who had ordered death to all male infants. Often he had thrilled to the saga of a

saga—*story*

worried young mother—and her sober husband—
who had stolen away into the land of Egypt with her
child.

"Many of us thought," the boy's father finished,
"that the child had been captured and slain by
Herod. Until a decade passed and we heard rumors
of a youth who bore his name, and who lectured in
a Temple at Jerusalem to a group of learned doctors. A few years ago we heard that this same youth,
grown older, had organized a band of men, that with
them he was journeying from place to place, preach-
ing and teaching and aiding the needy. And—" here
the boy's father had a habit of lowering his voice and
glancing furtively around the room—"there are some
who say that he is the Messiah, and that he performs
wonderful deeds, healing the halt and the blind and
the lepers—even raising the dead."

Once, at this point, the boy interrupted. "I would
that I might meet him," he had said with eagerness.
"I would that he might take the hump from my back
and make me strong and straight like other children."

It was growing cold on the hillside. The boy
drew the shawl closer about his tired body and
wished that he were not a shepherd. Shepherds led
a lonely life—they did not fit into the bright places
of the world. Rooms gaily lighted at eventide were

---

furtively—*secretly; in a sneaking manner*
halt—*lame*

for the men and boys who worked hard by day and earned their moments of ease; they were not for shepherds. But what else could a crippled lad do to justify his existence—what else than tend sheep?

Yawning wearily, the boy glanced at the sky. From the position of the moon, he judged it to be midnight—it was still a long while before sunrise; still hours before someone would come to take his place and he could limp home. And yet midnight had its compensations! For at that time he could break his fast and partake of the lunch that his mother had packed so neatly into a basket.

As he reached for the basket, as he opened it slowly, the boy was wondering what had been prepared for his refreshment. He found, to his satisfaction, that there was a flask of goat's milk, and nearly a loaf of crusty dark bread, and some yellow cheese; that there were dried figs, sugary with their own sweetness. And, wrapped separately, he came upon a real treat: a cake made of eggs and sifted flour, with citron in it, and raisins!

He had expected the bread and the cheese and the milk. Even the figs he had expected. But the cake was a surprise, the sort of surprise that happened seldom. His eyes gleamed as he surveyed it, and some

---

justify—*to give a good reason for*
compensations—*benefits; something that makes up for a loss*
citron—*a semitropical fruit*

of the sadness went out of them. Carefully he set the basket down and spread on the ground beside him the square of linen in which his mother had folded the lunch. Carefully he laid out the flask of milk, the bread, the cheese—but not the cake, which he left tucked away in the depths of the basket. He left it there so that he might not be tempted to eat it first.

"It is good to be hungry," he said aloud. "Yes—and to have food!"

From somewhere just behind him a voice spoke. It was not a loud voice, and yet the music of it seemed to carry beyond the hillside.

"Indeed, yes!" said the voice. "It is good to be hungry. And to have food, and to—"

Startled, for he had thought he was quite alone with his thoughts and the drowsing

sheep, the boy glanced back across his crooked shoulder. He saw a man standing upon the brow of the hill, silhouetted against the night sky. Ordinarily he would have known fear, for there were cruel robbers abroad often at midnight. But somehow the sight of this man failed to frighten him. He did not know why he instinctively completed the man's unfinished sentence.

"And to share it!" he murmured, as if in a dream. "You are a stranger, sir?"

The man came closer to the boy and stood looking down upon him. "No, not a stranger," he said slowly, "never a stranger. As it happens, my journey started not far from this very place—started years before you, my lad, saw the light."

"I was about to eat my lunch," the boy said, indicating the square of linen on which he had arranged the contents of his basket. "One grows hungry on the hillside. I am a shepherd, sir. I tend my father's flock, and each night my mother packs for me a simple meal. Will you be seated—you who have journeyed so long—and break bread with me? Perhaps—" he hesitated shyly—"you will talk with me as we eat? It grows lonely on the dark hillside. I long for companionship."

"I also tend my father's flock!" said the man. "And I also—" his smile was bright—"have often grown lonely waiting for the gates of dawn to open. Are you

sure—" he seated himself upon the ground—"that you have enough for two? I should not like to deprive you of anything."

Gazing, fascinated, into the man's face, the boy replied:

"But, yes! I have a large flask of goat's milk, and some yellow cheese, and nearly a loaf of bread, and ten figs. And—" for a second he hesitated—"that's a great plenty," he finished lamely. He did not mention the cake, still wrapped in the basket. For a cake—a cake made of sifted flour and eggs and citron and raisins—was a rare delicacy. And it was not a very big cake.

The man bent forward to retie the thong of a sandal. The boy saw that the sandal was covered with dust. He tried to keep his eyes from glancing toward his lunch basket as he tore the crusty dark bread into fragments.

"Perhaps your feet are aching," he ventured as he placed the fragments in the center of the linen cloth. "This hill is hard to climb. I am close to being spent when I reach the summit of it, but I must needs sit high so that I can watch all the sheep."

The man said slowly: "I have climbed steeper hills than this one, my lad, and know that there are steeper hills to be. My feet do not ache. How long—" abruptly he changed the subject— "have you been crippled?"

Had it come from an ordinary person, the boy would have resented such a display of curiosity. From this man the question seemed a natural one, to be answered naturally.

"Why," he said, "I have never been without a hump between my shoulders. I hate it, but—" he was quoting his mother—"what must be, must be! Still, it is hard to go through life looking like one of the camels that the Wise Men rode when they came from the east with their caravans—"

The man interrupted. "What, lad," he asked, "do you know of the Wise Men from the east? How does it happen that you should mention them to me on this night?"

Laughing softly, the boy answered. "I suppose the Wise Men are in my mind," he said, "because

---

ventured—*suggested*   **abruptly**—*suddenly*

this is the time of anniversary, and I have been
thinking of the baby that was born in a stable. I
was hoping—before you arrived—that once again
the great star might shine and that the angels might
sing. I have, in fact, been watching the sky rather
than the sheep."

The man asked another swift question. "What,"
he asked, "do you know about these holy things—
about the star and the song? You are so very young!"

The boy explained. "All Bethlehem," he said,
"heard about the star, and about the infant who lay in
the manger because there was no room at the inn. I
know, perhaps, more than the others, for my father—
a child then himself—was one of the shepherds who
saw the light from the heavens and heard the angel
music . . . Will you—" the boy had taken the flask of
goat's milk into his hands—"will you share with me
this cup, sir? For perhaps you thirst?"

"I will share the cup with you, my lad, for I do
thirst."

"Will you tell me, sir, of some of the towns in
which you have stayed?"

The man answered, "One town is very like another, my lad, with poverty and pain rubbing elbows
against wealth, with greed taking toll, all too often,
of humanity. With health on one side and illness on
the other. With so few gracious deeds that one can

do to help the sore distressed, and a lifetime in which to do them so desperately short!"

In a low tone the boy said, "Sometimes, when I was a tot, I hoped that my life might be short, but already I am ten years old. How old, sir, are you? I feel older than my years. . . . "

The man's voice was soft as he replied, "I am more than three times your age, lad, but I, too, feel older than my years."

"You shouldn't, because you're so strong," the boy exclaimed. "When is your time of birth, sir? I was born when it was spring."

The man smiled his beautiful, bright smile. "It's odd that you should ask, dear lad," he murmured, "for this is my day of birth. You, quite unknowing, are giving me an anniversary feast—and never has a feast been more welcome. I was weary when I came upon you."

Weary and forlorn! As he stared at the man, the boy asked:

"Haven't you any people of your own? People with whom you can make merry on your day of birth? When my birthday arrives, Mother prepares a *real* feast for me, and gives me gifts. This shawl I wear she wove for my last birthday. The year before she pressed a sheaf of bright flowers into wax. Once, when I was smaller, she made wondrous sweetmeats of honey and grain."

The man reached over and rested his hand on the little boy's knee. "I fear," he said, "that I have grown too old and large for birthday gifts. Furthermore, my loved ones are not near enough just now to make merry with me. But maybe, who knows, there will be a gift for me at my journey's end."

The boy's knee felt all atingle under the pressure of the friendly hand. He asked, "When, sir, will you come to your journey's end?"

The man did not meet the child's gaze. He replied, "Perhaps very soon!"

The boy was worried. He said: "You don't look happy about it. Don't you want to come to the end of your travels? Don't you want to reach home and see what gift they have in store for you?"

The man hesitated ever so slightly. "Yes," he said at last, "I want to reach—home." His face looked drawn in the white moonlight—"I should be getting on. You have made this birthday very sweet, my lad!"

Peeping down at the white cloth with its remnants of bread and cheese, the boy thought: "There seems to be as much food as ever! He couldn't have liked it." Suddenly he was swept by a burning sense of shame. He spoke quickly, one word tumbling over the other.

"You did not enjoy your food," he said, "and you have had no true birthday feast. That—though you have no way of guessing—is because I have been selfish and mean! I," he gulped out his confession, "have a cake in my basket—a cake that I was saving to eat alone after you left me. It is a cake of sifted flour and eggs and citron and raisins, *and I love cake.* But now," the boy's voice quavered, "I would not enjoy it if I ate it by myself; it would choke me! Sir, I desire to give the cake to you as my gift. Perhaps you will munch it later, when the chill of early morn has set in and you are on the road."

"Ah, my lad," he said, "you have sustained me with your bread, and we have drunk deep of the same cup. So now we will share this cake, which shall be, through your bounty, my birthday cake, and we will eat of it together—you and I. And then you shall wait for the dawn, and I will be on my way. But as I walk along the road, I shall see a little lad's face, and shall hear a little lad's voice, and shall remember a little lad's generosity."

So he and the boy ate the cake together, and the boy thought that he had never tasted such fare. As he licked the last crumbs from his fingers, he felt that he was gathering force and vigor and purpose. In his mind's eye, for no reason at all, he saw a picture of himself—robust and handsome and brave—

---

sustained—*provided nourishment*
robust—*healthy; strong*

striding down the road with his weakness cast from him and his chin high.

"It's like a vision!" he said, but when the man asked,

"What do you mean, lad?" he hung his head and was unable to answer.

Indeed, he was silent so long that the man's hand came to rest lightly upon his shoulder— lightly, but, oh, so firmly! There was something in the touch that made tears hang on the boy's lashes, that wrung from him quick words.

"Oh," he cried, "do not leave me, sir! We could be such friends, you and I. Come with me to my home and dwell with my family. My mother will bake many cakes for you, and my father will share with you of his plenty. And I—you may have my bed, and my waxed flowers, and even this fringed shawl that I wear. Do not journey on, sir! Stay with me, here in Bethlehem."

The man spoke. His voice was like a great bell tolling over hill and valley. "I must go on," he said. "I must be about my father's business—I must travel toward my destiny. But I shall never leave you, my lad, for all that. Lo, I am with you always—even unto the end of the world!"

Bowing his head in his hands, covering his misted eyes, the boy was aware of the man's firm fingers

traveling up from
his shoulder until
they touched his
hair. But now he
couldn't speak, for
a pulse drummed
in his throat, and
a strange rhythm
was hammering
in his ears. When
he raised his head,
finally, the man
was gone, and the
hillside was empty—
save for the shadows
that were the sheep.

The boy sobbed
once, and sharply, with
a sense of loss. He struggled to his feet. Only he
didn't have to struggle, really, for there was a curious lightness about his body, and a feeling of fresh-
ness and peace. But it was not until he drew the
fringed lamb's-wool shawl tighter across his back
that he realized how straight he was standing—
and how straight he would always stand.

Character Theme—Kindness & Sacrifice

Thinking It Through

1. What physical problem did the shepherd boy have?

2. What was the "anniversary" that the story refers to?

3. What surprise had the shepherd boy's mother put in his lunch?

4. What did the shepherd boy offer the stranger to eat? What didn't he offer the stranger to eat?

5. Do you think the shepherd boy would have enjoyed the cake as much if he had eaten it all by himself after the stranger had left?

6. Who do you think the stranger was?

7. How did the stranger reward the boy for his kindness and generosity?

From the Bible

And the angel said unto them, Fear not: for, behold, I bring you good tidings of great joy, which shall be to all people. For unto you is born this day in the city of David a Savior, which is Christ the Lord.   —Luke 2:10–11

For All

Thy cradle was a manger,
Thy lodging was a stall,
When Thou wast born into the world
Once and for all.

Thy steed it was a donkey,
Thy shelter Mary's shawl,
When Thou began'st Thy journeying
Once and for all.

Thy infancy was cloudless,
No tear didst Thou let fall,
Till time was come to weep for men
Once and for all.

—*Eleanor Farjeon*

MODERN MIRACLE

A little boy once long ago,
At even, ere the sun sank low,
Freely offered his meager food,
Which Thou didst take and bless and
   break,
And with it fed the multitude.

Dear Lord, with like simplicity
I bring and give my life to Thee
To bless and break as seems most good;
Then of it take, for Thy dear sake,
And use—to feed the multitude.

—William Atherton

even—*evening*
simplicity—*simpleness*

The Dove Who Spoke Truth

Abbie Farwell Brown

The dove and the wrinkled little bat once went on a journey together. When it came toward night, a storm arose, and the two companions sought everywhere for a shelter. But all the birds were sound asleep in their nests and the animals in their holes and dens. They could find no welcome anywhere until they came to the hollow tree where old Master Owl sat, wide awake in the dark.

"Let us knock here," said the shrewd bat. "I know the old fellow is not asleep. This is his prowling hour, and if it were not a stormy night, he would be out hunting. What ho, Master Owl!" he squeaked, "Will you let in two storm-tossed travelers for a night's lodging?"

Gruffly, the selfish old owl bade them enter, and grudgingly invited them to share his supper. The poor dove was so tired that she could scarcely eat, but the greedy bat's spirits rose as soon as

---

sought—*looked for*   **shrewd**—*clever*

he saw the food spread before him. He was a sly fellow, and he immediately began to flatter his host into good humor. He praised the owl's wisdom and his courage, his gallantry and his generosity; though everyone knew that however wise old Master Owl might be, he was neither brave nor generous.

All this flattery pleased the owl, however. He puffed and ruffled himself, trying to look as wise, gallant, and brave as possible. He pressed the bat to eat more, and the bat gladly accepted the offer.

During this time, the dove had not uttered a word. She sat quite still, staring at the bat, and wondering that he would use such flattery. Suddenly, the owl turned to her.

"As for you, Miss Pink-Eyes," he said gruffly, "you keep careful silence. You are a dull

host—*a man who entertains guests in his own home*
gallantry—*noble courage*

table companion. Pray, have you nothing to say for yourself?"

"Yes," exclaimed the mischievous bat; "have you no words of praise for our kind host? I think he deserves some return for this wonderfully generous, agreeable, tasteful, well-appointed, luxurious, elegant, and altogether acceptable banquet. What have you to say, O little dove?"

But the dove hung her head, ashamed of her companion, and said very simply, "O Master Owl, I can only thank you with all my heart for the hospitality and shelter which you have given me this night. I was beaten by the storm, and you took me in. I was hungry, and you gave me your best to eat. I cannot flatter nor make pretty speeches like the bat. I never learned such manners, but I thank you."

"What!" cried the bat, pretending to be shocked. "Is that all you have to say to our marvelous host? Is he not the wisest, bravest, most gallant and generous of gentlemen? Have you no praise for his noble character as well as for his goodness to us? I am ashamed of you! You do not deserve such hospitality. You do not deserve this shelter." The dove remained silent. She could not speak untruths even for her own happiness.

---

mischievous—*full of tricks*
hospitality—*friendly and generous entertainment of guests*

"You are an ungrateful bird, Miss," said the owl, "and the bat is right. You do not deserve this generous hospitality which I have offered, this goodly shelter which you asked. Away with you! Leave my dwelling!"

"Yes, away with her!" echoed the bat, flapping his leathery wings.

And the two heartless creatures fell upon the poor little dove and drove her out into the dark and stormy night.

Poor little dove! All night she was tossed and beaten about shelterless in the storm, because she had been too truthful to flatter the vain old owl. But when the bright morning dawned, draggled and weary as she was, she flew to the court of King Eagle and told him all her trouble. Great was the indignation of that noble bird.

"For his flattery and his cruelty let the bat never leave his nest until the sun goes down," he cried. "As for the owl, I have already doomed him to this punishment for his other unkind deeds. But henceforth let no bird have anything to do with either of them, the bat or the owl. Let them be outcasts and night-prowlers, enemies to be attacked and punished if they appear among us, to be avoided by all in their loneliness. Flattery and inhospitality, deceit and cruelty—what are more hideous than these?

Let them cover themselves in darkness and shun the happy light of day.

"As for you, little dove, let this be a lesson to you to stay away from flatterers, who are sure to get you into trouble. But you shall always be loved for your simplicity and truth. And as a token of our affection, your name shall be used by poets as long as the world shall last to rhyme with *love*."

Character Theme—Honesty & Humility

Thinking It Through

1. Why did the bat flatter the owl? Did he tell the truth?

2. Why did the dove refuse to flatter the owl? Do you think that the dove was unkind?

3. Why did the bat and the owl drive the dove away? Did she deserve to be treated unkindly?

4. What lesson did the dove learn?

From the Bible

Wherefore putting away lying, speak every man truth with his neighbor.

—Ephesians 4:25

Our Lips
&
Ears

If you your lips would keep from slips,
  Five things observe with care;
Of whom you speak, to whom you speak,
  And how and when and where.

If you your ears would save from jeers,
  These things keep meekly hid;
Myself and I, and mine and my,
  And how I do and did.

Little **Words** of *Kindness*

A little word in kindness spoken,
  A motion or a tear,
Has often healed the heart that's broken,
  And made a friend sincere.

A word, a look, has crushed to earth
  Full many a budding flower,
Which, had a smile but owned its birth,
  Would bless life's darkest hour.

Then think it not an idle thing
  A pleasant word to speak:
The face you wear, the thoughts you bring,
  A heart may heal or break.

Character Theme—Kindness

Eureka!

James Baldwin

> Would any man be strong, let him
> work; or wise, let him observe and think;
> or happy, let him help; or influential, let
> him sacrifice and serve.
> — *John Ruskin*

There was once a king of Syracuse whose
name was Hiero. The country over which
he ruled was quite small, but for that very reason he
wanted to wear the biggest crown in the world. So
he called in a famous goldsmith, who was skillful in
all kinds of fine work, and gave him ten pounds of
pure gold.

"Take this," he said, "and fashion it into a crown
that shall make every other king want it for his own.
Be sure that you put into it every grain of the gold I
give you, and do not mix any other metal with it."

"It shall be as you wish," said the goldsmith.
"Here I receive from you ten pounds of pure gold;
within ninety days I will return to you the finished
crown which shall be of exactly the same weight."

Eureka (yo͞o·rē′kə)
Syracuse (sĭr′ə·kyo͞os′)—*an ancient
city on the east coast of Sicily*

Hiero (hī′ə·rō)

Ninety days later, true to his word, the gold-smith brought the crown. It was a beautiful piece of work, and all who saw it said that it had not its equal in the world. When King Hiero put it on his head it felt very uncomfortable, but he did not mind that—he was sure that no other king had so fine a headpiece. After he had admired it from this side and from that, he weighed it on his own scales. It was exactly as heavy as he had ordered.

"You deserve a great praise," he said to the gold-smith. "You have wrought very skillfully and you have not lost a grain of my gold."

There was in the court a very wise man whose name was Archimedes. When he was called in to admire the king's crown he turned it over many times and examined it very closely.

"Well, what do you think of it?" asked Hiero.

"The workmanship is indeed very beautiful," answered Archimedes, "but—but the gold—"

"The gold is all there," cried the king. "I weighed it on my own scales."

"True," said Archimedes, "but it does not appear to have the same rich red color that it had in the lump. It is not red at all, but a brilliant yellow, as you can plainly see."

---

wrought—*worked*
Archimedes (är′kə·mē′dēz)—*a Greek mathematician and physicist*

"Most gold is yellow," said Hiero, "but now that you speak of it I do remember that when this was in the lump it had a much richer color."

"What if the goldsmith has kept out a pound or two of the gold and made up the weight by adding brass or silver?" asked Archimedes.

"Oh, he could not do that," said Hiero. "The gold has merely changed its color in the working."

But the more he thought of the matter the less pleased he was with the crown. At last he said to Archimedes, "Is there any way to find out whether that goldsmith really cheated me, or whether he honestly gave me back my gold?"

"I know of no way," was the answer.

But Archimedes was not the man to say that anything was impossible. He took great delight in working out hard problems, and when any question puzzled him he would keep studying until he found some sort of answer to it. And so, day after day, he thought about the gold and tried to find some way by which it could be tested without doing harm to the crown.

One morning he was thinking of this question while he was getting ready for a bath. The great bowl or tub was full to the very edge, and as he stepped into it a quantity of water flowed out upon

merely—*only*

190

the stone floor. A similar thing had happened a hundred times before, but this was the first time that Archimedes had thought about it.

"How much water did I displace by getting into the tub?" he asked himself. "Anybody can see that I displaced a bulk of water equal to the bulk of my body. A man half my size would displace half as much.

"Now suppose, instead of putting myself into the tub, I had put Hiero's crown into it, it would have displaced a bulk of water equal to its own bulk. Ah, let me see! Gold is much

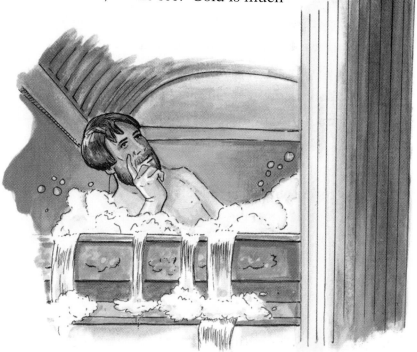

displace—*to take the place of; move (something) from its customary place*

heavier than silver. Ten pounds of pure gold will not make so great a bulk as say seven pounds of gold mixed with three pounds of silver. If Hiero's crown is pure gold it will displace the same bulk of water as any other ten pounds of pure gold. But if it is part gold and part silver it will displace a larger bulk. I have it at last! Eureka! Eureka!"

Forgetful of everything else, he leaped from the bath. Without stopping to dress himself, he ran through the streets to the king's palace shouting, "Eureka! Eureka! Eureka!" which means, "I have found it! I have found it! I have found it!"

The crown was tested. It was found to displace much more water than ten pounds of pure gold displaced. The guilt of the goldsmith was proved beyond a doubt. But whether he was punished or not, I do not know, neither does it matter.

The simple discovery which Archimedes made in his bathtub was worth far more to the world than Hiero's crown. Can you tell why?

Character Theme—Initiative, Perseverance, & Resourcefulness

---

bulk—*size, mass, or volume*

Thinking It Through

1. Was the goldsmith obedient to the king's command in making a beautiful crown?

2. How many pounds of gold were to be in the king's crown?

3. Was the goldsmith completely honest in the making of the crown? How was he dishonest?

4. Why was Archimedes not sure that the crown was pure gold?

5. What kind of thinker was Archimedes? How do you know?

Keep Trying

If boys should get discouraged
    At lessons or at work,
And say, "There's no use trying,"
    And all hard tasks should shirk,
And keep on shirking, shirking,
    Till the boy becomes a man,
I wonder what the world would do
    To carry out its plan?

shirk—*to neglect duty*

The coward in the conflict
    Gives up at first defeat;
If once repulsed, his courage
    Lies shattered at his feet.
The brave heart wins the battle;
    Because, through thick and thin,
He'll not give up as conquered;
    He fights, and fights to win.

So, boys, don't get disheartened
    Because at first you fail.
If you but keep on trying,
    At last you will prevail.
Be stubborn against failure;
    Try, try, and try again;
The boys who've kept on trying
    Have made the world's best men.

—Eben E. Rexford

---

prevail—*to have victory*

The Two Frogs

Aesop

Two frogs once fell into a can of cream. One of them, after a fruitless effort to scale the smooth perpendicular wall of the prison, gave up disheartened and sank to the bottom. The other would not give up but kept endeavoring again and again to scale the wall. His furious splashing finally made a little pat of butter, upon which he was found standing by the dairyman in the morning.

Character Theme—Perseverance

The Nightingale

Hans Christian Andersen
(adapted)

> The bird that soars on highest wing
>   Builds on the ground her lowly nest;
> And she that doth most sweetly sing
>   Sings in the shade when all things rest.
>   In lark and nightingale we see
>   What honor hath humility.
>   —*James Montgomery*

～The Emperor's Palace ～

In China, as you know, the Emperor is a Chinaman, and all the people around him are Chinamen too. It is many years since the story I am going to tell you happened, but that is all the more reason for telling it, lest it should be forgotten.

The Emperor's palace was the most beautiful thing in the world. It was made entirely of finest porcelain, which was very costly, and so fragile that it could be touched only with the very greatest of care. The most extraordinary flowers were to be seen in the garden. The most beautiful ones had little silver bells tied to them which tinkled perpetually, so that no one could pass the flowers without looking at them. Every little detail in the garden had been most

---

porcelain—*china*   perpetually—*constantly*

carefully thought out, and it was so big that even the gardener himself did not know where it ended.

If one went on walking, one came to beautiful woods with lofty trees and deep lakes. The wood extended to the sea, which was deep and blue, deep enough for large ships to sail up right under the branches of the trees. Among these trees lived a nightingale, which sang so deliciously that even the poor fisherman, who had plenty of other things to do, lay still to listen to it when he was out at night drawing in his nets.

"How beautiful it is," he said, but then he had to attend to his business and forgot it. The next night when he heard it again he would again exclaim, "How beautiful it is!"

Travelers came to the Emperor's capital from every country in the world. They admired every-thing very much, especially the palace and the gardens, but when they heard the nightingale they all said, "This is better than anything."

When they got home they described it, and learned men wrote many books about the town, the palace, and the garden. But nobody forgot the nightingale—it was always put above everything else. Those among them who were poets wrote the most beautiful poems, all about the nightingale in the woods by the deep blue sea. These books went all over the world, and in course of time some of them reached the Emperor. He sat in his golden chair reading and reading, and nodding his head, well pleased to hear such beautiful descriptions of the town, the palace, and the garden. "But the nightingale is the best of all," he read.

"What is this?" said the Emperor. "The nightingale? Why, I know nothing about it. Is there such a bird in my kingdom, and in my own garden, and I have never heard of it? Imagine my having to discover this from a book."

Then he called his gentleman-in-waiting, who was so grand that when anyone of a lower rank dared to speak to him or to ask him a question, he would only answer, "P," which means nothing at all.

"There is said to be a very wonderful bird called a nightingale here," said the Emperor. "They say that it is better than anything else in all my great kingdom. Why have I never been told anything about it?"

"I have never heard it mentioned," said the gentleman-in-waiting. "It has never been presented at court."

"I wish it to appear here this evening to sing to me," said the Emperor. "The whole world knows what I am possessed of, and I know nothing about it!"

"I have never heard it mentioned before," said the gentleman-in-waiting. "I will seek it, and I will find it." But where was it to be found? The gentleman-in-waiting ran upstairs and downstairs and in and out of all the rooms and corridors. No one of all those he met had ever heard anything about the nightingale. So the gentleman-in-waiting ran back to the Emperor and said that it must be a myth, invented by the writers of the books. "Your Imperial Majesty must not believe everything that is written! Books are often mere inventions, even if they do not belong to what we call the black art."

"But the book in which I read it was sent to me by the powerful Emperor of Japan. Therefore it can't be untrue. I will hear this nightingale. I insist upon its being here tonight. I extend my most gracious protection to it, and if it is not forthcoming, I will have the whole court trampled upon after supper."

～The Search for the Nightingale ～

The gentleman-in-waiting ran again, up and down all the stairs, in and out of all the rooms and corridors. Half the court ran with him, for none of them wished to be trampled on. There was much questioning about this nightingale, which was known to all the outside world but to no one at court.

---

corridors—*hallways*

200

At last they found a poor little maid in the kitchen, who said, "Oh heavens! The nightingale? I know it very well. Yes, indeed, it can sing. Every evening I am allowed to take broken meat to my poor sick mother who lives down by the shore. On my way back, when I am tired I rest awhile in the wood, and then I hear the nightingale. Its song brings the tears into my eyes. I feel as if my mother were kissing me."

"Little kitchen maid," said the gentleman-in-waiting, "I will procure you a permanent position in the kitchen and permission

procure—*to obtain; get*

to see the Emperor dining, if you will take us to the nightingale. It is commanded to appear at court tonight."

Then they all went out into the wood where the nightingale usually sang. Half the court was there. As they were going along at their best pace, a cow began to bellow.

"Oh," said a young courtier, "there we have it. What wonderful power for such a little creature. I have certainly heard it before."

"No, those are the cows bellowing. We are a long way from the place." Then frogs began to croak in the marsh.

"How beautiful!" said the Chinese chaplain. "It is just like the tinkling of church bells."

"No, those are the frogs," said the little kitchen maid. "But I think we shall soon hear it now."

Then the nightingale began to sing.

"Listen, Listen! There it sits," said the little girl. And she pointed to a little gray bird up among the branches.

"Is it possible?" said the gentleman-in-waiting. "I should never have thought it was like that. How common it looks. Seeing so many grand people must have frightened all its colors away."

---

chaplain—*a minister*

"Little nightingale," called the kitchen maid quite loudly. "Our Gracious Emperor wishes you to sing to him."

"With the greatest pleasure," said the nightingale, warbling away in the most delightful fashion.

"It is just like crystal bells," said the gentleman-in-waiting. "Look at its little throat, how active it is. It is extraordinary that we have never heard it before. I am sure it will be a great success at court."

"Shall I sing again to the Emperor?" said the nightingale, who thought he was present.

"My precious little nightingale," said the gentleman-in-waiting, "I have the honor to command your attendance at a court festival tonight, where you will charm His Gracious Majesty the Emperor with your fascinating singing."

"It sounds best among the trees," said the nightingale, but it went with them willingly when it heard that the Emperor wished it.

∾ The Court Festival ∾

The palace had been brightened up for the occasion. The walls and the floors, which were all of china, shone by the light of many thousand golden lamps. The most beautiful flowers, all of the tinkling kind, were arranged in the corridors. There was hurrying to and fro, and a great draft, but this was just what made the bells ring. One's ears were full of the tinkling. In the middle of the large reception room where the emperor sat, a golden rod had been fixed, on which the nightingale was to perch. The whole court was assembled, and the little kitchen maid had been permitted to stand behind the door, as she now had the actual title of Cook. They were all dressed in their best. Everybody's eyes were turned toward the little gray bird at which the Emperor was nodding.

The nightingale sang delightfully, and the tears came into the Emperor's eyes and rolled down his cheeks. And when the nightingale sang more beautifully than ever, its notes melted all hearts. The Emperor was so charmed that he said the nightingale should have his gold slipper to wear round its neck. But the nightingale declined with thanks—it had already been sufficiently rewarded.

"I have seen tears in the eyes of the Emperor," he said. "That is my richest reward. The tears of an Emperor have a wonderful power. God knows I am sufficiently recompensed." And it again burst into its sweet heavenly song.

"That is the most delightful sound I have ever heard!" said the ladies. And they took some water into their mouths to try and make the same gurgling, when anyone spoke to them, thinking so to equal the nightingale. Even the lackeys and the chambermaids announced that they were satisfied, and that is saying a great deal. They were always the most difficult people to please. Yes, indeed, the nightingale had made a sensation. It was to stay at court now, and have its own cage, as well as liberty to walk out twice a day and once in the night. It always had twelve footmen, with each one holding

---

recompensed—*repaid; rewarded*

a ribbon which was tied round its leg. There was not much pleasure in an outing of that sort.

The whole town talked about the marvelous bird. If two people met, one said "Night," and the other answered, "Gale." And they sighed, perfectly understanding each other. Eleven cheesemongers' children were named after it, but not one among them could sing anything.

∾ The Artificial Bird ∾

One day a large parcel came for the Emperor. Outside was written the word "Nightingale."

"Here we have another new book about this celebrated bird," said the Emperor. But it was not a book. It was a little work of art in a box, an artificial nightingale exactly like the living one, except that it was studded all over with diamonds, rubies, and sapphires.

When the artificial bird was wound up, it could sing one of the songs the real one sang, and it wagged its tail, which glittered with silver and gold. A ribbon was tied round its neck on which was written, "The Emperor of Japan's nightingale is very poor compared to the Emperor of China's."

Everybody said, "Oh, how beautiful!" And the person who brought the artificial bird immediately received the title of Imperial Nightingale-Carrier-in-Chief.

"Now, they must sing together. What a duet that will be!"

Then they had to sing together, but they did not get on very well, for the real nightingale sang in its own way and the artificial one could only sing waltzes.

"There is no fault in that," said the music master. "It is perfectly in time and correct in every way."

Then the artificial bird had to sing alone. It was just as great a success as the real one, and it was much prettier to look at, because it glittered like bracelets and breastpins.

It sang the same tune three and thirty times over, and yet it was not tired. People would willingly have heard it from the beginning again, but the Emperor said that the real one must have a turn now. But where was it? No one had noticed that it had flown out of the open window, back to its own green woods.

"What is the meaning of this?" said the Emperor.

All the courtiers railed at it and said it was a most ungrateful bird.

"We have got the best bird though," said they, and then the artificial bird had to sing again. This was the thirty-fourth time that they had heard the same tune, but they did not know it thoroughly even yet because it was so difficult.

The music master praised the bird tremendously and insisted that it was better than the real nightingale, not only on the outside with all its diamonds, but inside too.

"You see, my ladies and gentlemen, and the Emperor before all, in the real nightingale you never know what you will hear, but in the artificial one everything is decided beforehand. So it is, and so it must remain. It can't be otherwise. You can account for things: you can open it and show the human ingenuity in arranging how the waltzes go, and how one note follows upon another."

"Those are exactly my opinions," they all said, and the music master got leave to show the bird to the public next Sunday. They were also to hear it sing, said the Emperor. So they heard it, and all became as enthusiastic over it as if they had drunk themselves merry on tea, because that is a thoroughly Chinese habit.

Then they all said, "Oh!" and stuck their fore-fingers in the air and nodded their heads. But the poor fisherman who had heard the real nightingale said, "It sounds very nice, and it is very nearly like the real one, but there is something wanting. I don't know what." The real nightingale was banished from the kingdom.

---

ingenuity—*cleverness; skill*   banished—*sent away*

The artificial bird
had its place on a silken
cushion, close to the
Emperor's bed. All
the presents it had
received of gold and
precious jewels were
scattered round it.
Its title had risen to
be Chief Imperial Singer-of-
the-Bed-Chamber. In rank it stood
number one on the left side, for the Emperor reckoned that side where the heart was seated was the
important one. And even an Emperor's heart is on
the left side.

The music master wrote five and twenty vol-
umes about the artificial bird. The treatise was
very long, and was written in all the most difficult
Chinese characters. Everybody said they had read
and understood it, for otherwise they would have
been reckoned dull, and then their bodies would
have been trampled upon.

Things went on in this way for a whole year.
The Emperor, the court, and all the other Chinamen
knew every little gurgle in the song of the artificial
bird by heart. But they liked it all the better for

treatise—*an essay; book*

this, and they could all join in the song themselves.
Even the street boys sang "Zizizi! cluck, cluck!" And
the Emperor sang it too.

But one evening, when the bird was singing
its best and the Emperor was lying in bed listening to it, something gave way inside the bird with
a "Whizz." "Whirr!" went all the wheels, and the
music stopped.

The Emperor jumped out of bed and sent for
his private physicians, but what good could they
do? Then they sent for the watchmaker, who after
a good deal of talk and examination got the works
to go again somehow. But he said the bird would
have to be spared as much as possible, because it
was so worn out, and that he could not renew the
works so as to be sure of the tune. This was a great
blow! They now dared to let the artificial bird sing
only once a year, and hardly that. But then the music master made a little speech using all the most
difficult Chinese words. He said it was just as good
as ever, and his saying it made it so.

∼Grief∼

Five years passed, and then a great grief came
upon the nation. They were all very fond of their
Emperor, and now he was ill and could not live,
it was said. A new Emperor was already chosen,
and people stood about in the street and asked the

gentleman-in-waiting how the Emperor was getting on.

"P," answered he, shaking his head.

The Emperor lay pale and cold in his gorgeous bed. The courtiers thought he was dead, and they all went off to pay their respects to their new Emperor. The lackeys ran off to talk matters over, and the chambermaids gave a great coffee party. Cloth had been laid down in all the rooms and corridors so as to deaden the sounds of footsteps, so it was very, very quiet. But the Emperor was not dead yet. He lay stiff and pale in the gorgeous bed with velvet hangings and heavy golden tassels. There was an open window high above him, and the moon streamed in upon the Emperor and the artificial bird beside him.

∼Song∼

Suddenly, close to the window there was a burst of lovely song. It was the living nightingale, perched on a branch outside. It had heard of the Emperor's need and had come to bring comfort and hope to him. As it sang, the blood coursed with fresh vigor in the Emperor's veins and through his feeble limbs. It sang about the quiet churchyard where the roses bloom, where the elder flowers scent the air, and where the fresh grass is ever moistened anew by the tears of the mourners.

---

vigor—*strength; energy*

"Thanks, thanks!" said the Emperor. "You heavenly little bird, I know you. I banished you from my kingdom, and yet you have charmed Death away from my heart. How can I ever repay you?"

"You have rewarded me," said the nightingale. "I brought tears to your eyes the very first time I ever sang to you, and I shall never forget it. Those are the jewels which gladden the heart of a singer. But sleep now, and wake up fresh and strong. I will sing to you."

Then it sang again, and the Emperor fell into a sweet refreshing sleep. The sun shone in at his window, and he awoke refreshed and well. None of his attendants had yet come back to him, for they thought he was dead, but the nightingale still sat there singing.

"You must always stay with me," said the Emperor. "You shall sing only when you like, and I will break the artificial bird into a thousand pieces."

"Don't do that," said the nightingale. "It did all the good it could. Keep it as you have always done. I can't build my nest and live in this palace, but let me come whenever I like. Then I will sit on the branch in the evening and sing to you. I will sing to cheer you and to make you thoughtful, too. I will sing to you of the happy ones and of those that suffer. I will sing about the good and the evil, which are kept hidden from you. The little singing bird flies far and wide, to the poor fisherman and to the peasant's home, to numbers who are far from you and your court. I love your heart more than your crown, and yet there is an odor of sanctity round the crown too! I will come, and I will sing to you. But you must promise me one thing."

"Everything!" said the Emperor, who stood there in his imperial robes which he had just put on, and he held the sword heavy with gold upon his heart.

---

sanctity—*holiness; purity*

"Only one thing I ask you. Tell no one that you have a little bird who tells you everything. It will be better so."

Then the nightingale flew away. The attendants came in to look after their dead Emperor—and there he stood, bidding them "Good morning!"

Character Theme—Beauty, Contentment, & Kindness

Thinking It Through

1. Where did the Emperor hear of the Nightingale? Who found the bird for the Emperor?

2. Was the Nightingale a beautiful bird?

3. Why were the people so pleased with the artificial bird?

4. Who finally sang for the Emperor while he lay on his death bed?

5. Which bird would you rather have? Why?

Flat Tail, the Beaver

Edward Eggleston

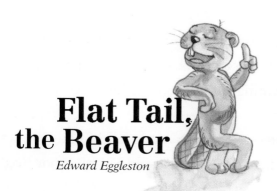

A colony of beavers selected a beautiful spot on a clear stream, called Silver Creek, to build themselves a home. Without waiting for any orders, and without any wrangling about whose place was the best, they gnawed down some young trees and laid the foundation for a dam. With that skill for which they are so remarkable, they built it so that it would protect them from cold, from water, and from their foes. When it was completed, they were delighted with it, and paddled round joyously in the pond above, expressing their pleasure to each other in true beaver style.

In this colony there was one young beaver by the name of Flat Tail. His father, whose name was Mud Dauber, had been a celebrated beaver, who, having very superior teeth, could gnaw through trees with great rapidity. Old Mud Dauber had distinguished himself chiefly, however, by saving the dam on three separate occasions in time of flood. He had done

---

wrangle—*to quarrel loudly*
rapidity—*speed*

distinguished—*made (himself) famous*

this by his courage and wisdom, always beginning to work as soon as he saw the danger coming, without waiting till the damage had become too great to repair.

But his son, this young fellow Flat Tail, was a sorry fellow. As long as old Mud Dauber lived, he did pretty well, but as soon as his father died, Flat Tail began to think that he was somebody great. Whenever anyone questioned his pretensions, he always replied, "I am Mud Dauber's son. I belong to the best blood in the colony."

He utterly refused to gnaw or build. He was meant for something better, he said.

And so one day in autumn, when the beavers were going out in search of food for winter use, as Flat Tail was good for nothing else, they set him to mind the dam. After they had started, Flat Tail's

---

pretention—*a proud show*

uncle, old Mr. Webfoot, turned back and told his nephew to be very watchful, as there had been a great rain on the headwaters of Silver Creek, and he was afraid there would be a flood.

"Be very careful," said Webfoot, "about the small leaks."

"Whom are you talking to?" said Flat Tail. "I am Mud Dauber's son, and do you think I need your advice?"

After they had gone, the stream began to rise. Little sticks and leaves were eddying round in the pool above. Soon the water came up faster, to the great delight of the conceited young beaver, who was pleased with the opportunity to show the rest what kind of stuff he was made of. And though he disliked work, he now began to strengthen the dam in the middle where the water looked the most threatening. But just at this point the dam was the strongest, and, in fact, the least in danger. Near the shore there was a place where the water was already finding its way through. A friendly kingfisher who sat on a neighboring tree warned him that the water was coming through, but, always too conceited to listen to advice, he answered:

"Oh, that's only a small leak, and near the shore. What does a kingfisher know about a beaver dam, anyway! You needn't advise me! I am the great Mud

---

eddying—*whirling*   **conceited**—*proud*

Dauber's son. I shall fight the stream bravely, right here in the worst of the flood."

But Flat Tail soon found that the water in the pond was falling. Looking round for the cause, he saw that the small leak had broken away a large portion of the dam, and that the torrent was rushing through it wildly.

Poor Flat Tail now worked like a hero, throwing himself wildly into the water only to be carried away below and forced to walk up again on the shore. His efforts were of no avail, and had not the rest of the Silver Creek beaver family come along at that time, their home and their winter's stock of provisions would all have been destroyed.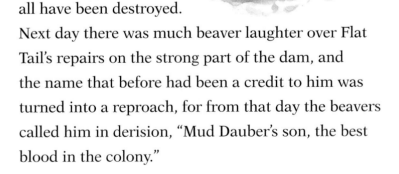

Next day there was much beaver laughter over Flat Tail's repairs on the strong part of the dam, and the name that before had been a credit to him was turned into a reproach, for from that day the beavers called him in derision, "Mud Dauber's son, the best blood in the colony."

---

torrent—*a rapid flood of water*   derision—*ridicule*
avail—*help; use*

Don't neglect a danger because it is small; don't boast of what your father did; and don't be too conceited to receive good advice.

Character Theme—Humility & Industry

Thinking It Through

1. What did the dam provide for the beavers?

2. How did Mud Dauber distinguish himself? Why was he able to save the dam?

3. What did Flat Tail boast about?

4. Why didn't Flat Tail take the Kingfisher's advice?

From the Bible

For I say, through the grace given unto me, to every man that is among you, not to think of himself more highly than he ought to think.

Let another man praise thee, and not thine own mouth; a stranger, and not thine own lips.

—*Romans 12:3; Proverbs 27:2*

The Village Blacksmith

If the power to do hard work is not talent,
it is the best possible substitute for it.
—*James Garfield*

Under a spreading chestnut tree
    The village smithy stands;
The smith, a mighty man is he,
    With large and sinewy hands;
And the muscles of his brawny arms
    Are strong as iron bands.

His hair is crisp and black and long;
    His face is like the tan;
His brow is wet with honest sweat,—
    He earns whate'er he can;
And looks the whole world in the face,
    For he owes not any man.

---

sinewy—*muscular*

Week in, week out, from morn till night,
  You can hear his bellows blow;
You can hear him swing his heavy sledge
  With measured beat and slow,
Like a sexton ringing the village bell,
  When the evening sun is low.

And children, coming home from school,
  Look in at the open door;
They love to see the flaming forge,
  And hear the bellows roar,
And catch the burning sparks that fly
  Like chaff from a threshing-floor.

He goes on Sunday to the church,
  And sits among his boys;
He hears the parson pray and preach,
  He hears his daughter's voice,
Singing in the village choir,
  And it makes his heart rejoice.

It sounds to him like her mother's voice,
  Singing in Paradise!
He needs must think of her once more,
  How in the grave she lies;
And with his hard, rough hand he wipes
  A tear out of his eyes.

---

bellows—*a machine that pumps air into a fire*
forge—*a furnace where metals are melted*

Toiling, rejoicing, sorrowing,
  Onward through life he goes;
Each morning sees some task begun,
  Each evening sees it close;
Something attempted, something done,
  Has earned a night's repose.

Thanks, thanks to thee, my worthy friend,
  For the lesson thou hast taught!
Thus at the flaming forge of life
  Our fortunes must be wrought;
Thus on its sounding anvil shaped
  Each burning deed and thought!
                              —*Henry W. Longfellow*

                    Character Theme—Faithfulness
                              & Industry

---

repose—*rest*

Andy's Monument

Stella C. Shetter

To be constantly employed, and
never asking, "What shall I do?"
is the secret of much goodness
and happiness.

—*Charlotte M. Yonge*

Bobby and Alice and Pink had been telling
Grandma about the soldiers' monument
that was to be placed in the courthouse yard.

"It is to be made of granite," said Bobby, "and the
names of all the soldiers from this county who died
or were killed in the war will be cut on one side of
it."

"Well, well," said Grandma thoughtfully, "that
makes me think of a monument I knew about long
ago, but this monument wasn't made of granite."

"Marble, maybe," suggested Alice.

"No, not marble, either. You never heard of a
monument like this. But, there, I might as well tell
you about it," and Grandma polished her spectacles,
found her knitting, and began:

"This monument was for a soldier, too. Andy
Carson was his name. He was a very young soldier,

---

granite—*hard, gray rock*   spectacles—*glasses*

only fifteen years old, but large for his age, and he ran away from home and enlisted. Three times he ran away, and twice his father brought him back, but the third time he let him go.

"But poor Andy never wore a uniform or saw a battle. He died in camp two weeks after he had enlisted and he was buried in our cemetery, with only Father to read a chapter out of the Bible and say a prayer, because the preacher was clear at the other end of the circuit.

"Right away Mrs. Carson began to plan for a monument for Andy. At first it was to be just an ordinary monument, but the more she thought about it, the grander she wanted it to be. Nothing could be too good for Andy. He should have the biggest monument in the cemetery—a life-size figure. But she couldn't decide whether to have the figure draped in a robe with a dove perched on the shoulder or to have it wearing a uniform and cap. Mrs. Carson finally settled on the uniform, though she couldn't give up the idea of the dove, so there was to be a dove in one outstretched hand.

"But the Carsons had no money, and they didn't like to work. If anyone mentioned work to Mr. Carson, he would begin always to talk about the

---

enlist—*join*
circuit—*the regular journey of a preacher who serves several towns*

misery in his back. When brother Charlie had a job he didn't want to do, he would bend over with his hand on his back, screw up his face as if he were in great pain, and say, 'Oh, that misery in my back!'

"Mother said Mrs. Carson had not been lazy as a girl, but that she had grown discouraged from having so many to do for and nothing to do with. Sometimes she came to visit Mother, because Mother was always nice to everybody. She was very tall and thin, with a short waist, and she wore the longest skirts I ever saw and a black slat sunbonnet.

"There was a big family of children—a girl, Maggie, older than Andy, and Willie, a boy a year younger, and four or five smaller children. The older ones came to school part of the time, but none of them ever came to church—partly because they had no proper clothes, I suppose.

"They lived on a farm left them by Mrs. Carson's father. The land was all run down and worn out. It was covered with briars and broom sage and a stubby growth of trees. Fences were down, and the buildings were unpainted and old.

"So, though the Carsons talked a great deal about Andy's monument, no one ever thought they would get one. But Mother said it was the first thing Mrs. Carson had really wanted for years and

years, and people generally got the things they
wanted most if they were willing to work hard for
them. And it turned out that all the Carsons were
willing to work hard for Andy's monument. It was
astonishing the way they worked.

"Mrs. Carson and the children started with
the house and yard. They cleaned the rubbish off
the yard and raked and swept it and planted flowers. They made the stove wood into a neat pile
and swept up the chips and patched the fence and
whitewashed it. By this time Mr. Carson had the
fever, too. He started to clear off the land, with
all the family helping him. All summer long they
worked, early and late, cutting out the briars and
underbrush, burning
broom sage, building
fences, and by fall

you wouldn't have known it for the same place. They worked for a number of other people, too, and made a little money, besides taking seed corn and a pair of little pigs and other things they needed in payment.

"Well, it took a lot of money for a monument like Andy's was to be, but the Carsons worked and saved for it. It seemed as if they had set a new standard for themselves and were trying hard to live up to Andy's monument.

"They painted the house and repaired and whitewashed the outbuildings and put a fence around the front yard. They got lace curtains and a store carpet for their best room, and when Father got us a piano, Mrs. Carson bought our organ for a trifle. They got new clothes and dishes and table-cloths, and every Sunday they all came to church and asked folks home with them to dinner just as anybody else did.

"Dave Orbison was courting Maggie, and Willie was ready to go to the academy. He wanted an education, and he came to our house every week to get Truman to help him with his studies or to borrow books. If it hadn't been for the monument, people would have forgotten that the Carsons had ever been considered lazy or shiftless.

shiftless—*not making any effort*

"But Mrs. Carson was always talking about the monument. She had never had Andy's funeral sermon preached, and she planned to have it preached the Sunday after the monument was set up.

"At the end of three years they had enough money, but for some reason they didn't get the monument. Everybody wondered about it. Weeks went by, and still no news of the monument. Willie often came to our house but he never mentioned it. Then one day Mrs. Carson came. She had a horse now, and she looked longer and thinner than ever in her black calico riding skirt.

"Mother was fitting a dress on me—a red wool delaine for Sundays—but Mrs. Carson dropped into a chair without even glancing at it.

"'Mrs. Purviance,' she began immediately, 'I want your honest opinion about something. For over three years now we've been saving for Andy's monument, and until a few weeks ago I never had a thought but that that was the right thing to do with the money. But one night I got to thinking that here was Willie wanting an education, and Maggie getting ready to be married and no money to help her set up housekeeping, and Lissy longing for music lessons, and I couldn't sleep for thinking. And, Mrs. Purviance, I haven't had a minute's peace since. That's why I

Mrs. Purviance (pûr′vē·əns)   delaine—*a lightweight wool cloth*

228

haven't ordered the monument. I can't make up my mind to it. It'll be a long time before we can help Willie much if we spend the monument money. It looks as if he ought to have his chance. And of course the money won't help Andy any, but I had set my heart on a fine monument for him. I don't know what to do,' and she started to cry.

"'Mrs. Carson,' Mother said gently, and there were tears in her eyes, too, 'if you want to know what I really think, I'll tell you. I think that as far as honoring Andy is concerned, you and your family have already given him a much better monument than any you can ever set up in the cemetery.'

"Mother ran a pin straight into me and I jumped, and Mother said she was done with me for a while. I went out, and that was the last I heard of the monument until the Sunday Andy's funeral sermon was to be preached.

"There had been so much talk about the monument and the long-delayed funeral sermon that there was an unusually large crowd at the church that day.

"And some of them were disappointed, for when the service was over and we filed out, the Carsons first, past the flower-decked graves to the corner where Andy was buried, there was Andy's grave adorned with only a plain little headstone. But grouped around it stood his family, and the way that family had improved in the three years since Andy's death—well, as my mother said, that was a pretty fine monument for Andy, don't you think so?"

ANDY CARSON
DIED
May 15, 1862
AGE
15 yrs

Character Theme—Aspirations, Love of Family, & Self-Discipline

Thinking It Through

1. What kind of monument did the Carsons want for Andy?

2. Why did the Carsons suddenly start to work?

3. How long did they have to work to get enough money for the monument?

4. Why did Mrs. Carson hesitate about ordering the monument?

5. Explain what Mrs. Purviance meant when she told Mrs. Carson, "You and your family have already given Andy a much better monument than any you can ever set up in the cemetery."

Flying

I saw the moon,
One windy night,
Flying so fast—
All silvery white—
Over the sky
Like a toy balloon
Loose from its string—
A runaway moon.
The frosty stars
Went racing past,
Chasing her on
Ever so fast.
Then everyone said,
"It's the clouds that fly,
And the stars and moon
Stand still in the sky."
But I don't mind—
I saw the moon
Sailing away
Like a toy
Balloon.

—*J. M. Westrup*

Ringing
in the 4th
of July   *Carolyn Sherwin Bailey*

Yesterday the greatest question was
decided which ever was debated in America; and a greater
perhaps never was, nor will be, decided among men. A
resolution was passed without one dissenting colony, that
these United Colonies are, and of right ought to be, free
and independent states.   *—John Adams*

The bell ringer of the statehouse in Philadelphia was growing old, and once in a while
his grandson climbed the stairs to the belfry and
pulled the bell rope to help him. It was a long, dark
way up the dusty staircase, and the lad always went
as quietly as his copper-toed shoes would let him,
partly so as not to surprise the mice and bats into
coming down to meet him, and partly to avoid dis-
turbing the great men of the country who met in the
assembly room of the statehouse.

They were the important statesmen of the American colonies, old Dr. Benjamin Franklin, who could
accomplish almost anything from printing an
almanac to catching lightning, and Mr. Thomas
Jefferson, who was looked up to as the wise scribe

---

belfry—*a tower or steeple that holds bells*
almanac—*a yearly calendar containing useful information*
scribe—*a writer; author*

of the colonies. His desk in the statehouse was so covered with quill pens and papers and red seals that the lad scarcely dared to dust it. There was also Mr. John Adams of Massachusetts, who had seen a shipload of bales of tea turned overboard in Boston Harbor three years before because the colonists refused to pay a tax on it to King George III of England. John Adams loved a cup of fragrant tea served in Boston's blue and white china, but he loved his country more.

On his way up toward the belfry stairs, the bell ringer's grandson peered in the door at these men and those others with them in knee breeches, silver-buckled shoes, and powdered hair. They were the members of the first American Congress, and their talk was of the colonies they represented, stretching now from Maine to Georgia; what was best for them in the way of government that the people might be free and yet united. The idea had already come to this first body of lawmakers that laws should not be made to limit a man's freedom, but to give men new liberty to live and work and think by freeing them from wrongdoing, lawlessness, and crime.

This matter of governing a new nation was becoming increasingly important. The Congress realized that, and so it was sitting in the statehouse of old Philadelphia on a very warm summer afternoon, the fourth of July in the year 1776.

The lad turned away from the door. Perhaps it would be better not to ring the bell for sunset, because the Congress was sitting so late, he decided. His grandfather was up in the belfry polishing the bell, and he would wait and go up when the gentlemen of the Congress started home. The boy stood a little while in the doorway of the brick building and looked down Chestnut Street on which it stood.

There came the post rider, his mail pouches gray with dust, and his horse's hoofs striking sparks on the paving stones in the warm, gathering twilight. What an adventuresome life a post rider's was, the lad thought enviously. They rode between all the cities of the new nation, meeting at the borders of the colonies to exchange and carry on letters and packets.

The post riders were making and living the geography of the American colonies, which were too young and were growing up too fast to be between book covers or on maps yet in the schools. They rode to the green pasture land of New Hampshire, heard the whir of spinning wheels in Connecticut, and passed the gate of Harvard College in Boston. They talked to the fishermen of Rhode Island and the trappers of New York, stopped for foaming mugs of milk in some dairy of New Jersey or Pennsylvania, passed fertile farms of Delaware and Maryland, had supper of hot corn bread and ham on a rich Virginia tobacco plantation, and rode past white cotton fields in the Carolinas or Georgia. The thirteen thriving, growing, alert American colonies were alike in their desire for liberty, and different in their settlement, people, work, products, and mode of thinking. But they were keeping together after a fashion, for they all sent delegates to the Continental Congress here in Philadelphia, and they were united at heart in a league of neighborly friendship and for common defense.

The post rider was gone now. The lad in the door of the statehouse could see nothing but a cloud of gray dust up Chestnut Street where he had been. It was the quiet, dim end of a sultry day and the street

---

delegate—*a person sent to represent others at a meeting*   sultry—*hot and moist*

was empty, for the early supper tables would soon be laid. At least Chestnut Street had been empty. Now the boy saw that it was suddenly beginning to fill. Housewives who had neglected to take off their cooking aprons, shopkeepers with their tape measures still dangling over their shoulders, a raw recruit of a soldier who held his musket awkwardly because his hands were more used to a spade, a barrister in a long black robe and huge wig, even the post rider returned; all these and more moved toward the stately old building that housed the Congress. What could it mean, the bell ringer's grandson wondered, shrinking back into the shadow of the doorway?

As he waited, the door of the assembly room opened, and he saw that Mr. Thomas Jefferson held in his hand a very long and important-looking document from which he was reading in his strong, clear voice. The boy could catch some of the words, and so could that part of the crowd outside nearest the open windows:

"When, in the course of human events, it becomes necessary for one people to dissolve the political bands which have connected them with another, and to assume, among the powers of the earth, the separate and equal station to which the

---

recruit—*a newly enlisted soldier*   barrister—*a lawyer*

laws of nature and of nature's God entitle them—"
Mr. Jefferson read. He went on:—

"We, therefore, the representatives of the United
States of America in general Congress assembled,
appealing to the Supreme Judge of the world for
the rectitude of our intentions, do, in the name, and
by authority of the good people of these colonies,
solemnly publish and declare, that these United
colonies are, and of right ought to be free and independent states."

That was the word that held the crowd breathless, "independent."

Then Mr. Jefferson finished:—

"That as free and independent States, they have
full power to levy war, conclude peace, contract
alliances, establish commerce, and to do all other
acts and things which independent States may do.
And, for the support of this declaration, with a firm
reliance on the protection of Divine Providence, we
mutually pledge to each other our lives, our fortunes, and our sacred honor."

There was a silence of only a second. Then the
ayes of the Congress, pledging the new nation's support to this Declaration of Independence filled the
room, and resounded in the street and re-echoed
from the crowd, mingling with their cheers.

---

rectitude—*strict honesty; correctness*
levy—*to wage (war)*

alliance—*a uniting for a
specific purpose*

"Ring the bell for freedom!" someone shouted.

Now his chance had come to celebrate the Fourth of July, 1776, the bell ringer's grandson knew, and he ran up the stairs to the belfry, kicking up almost as much dust as the post rider and not one whit afraid of the scurrying mice and the flapping winged bats.

"Ring the bell, Grandfather," he cried, "Ring it, the Congress and the people say, for freedom!"

Taking hold of the rope, the lad pulled too, helping his grandfather with all his might as peal after peal rang out through the summer evening as a signal for more shouts of joy in the street and the pealing of every other bell in old Philadelphia.

There are Christmas bells that chime for peace, and church bells that call us to think of holy things. The jester jingles his bells for mirth, and the sheep bells tinkling along country lanes at sunset tell us of the plenty and comfort of the farm. But the ringing of the Liberty Bell on that first Fourth of July held the message of all these others. It sounded the desire for a day when wars would not be needed. It rang for religious and civil liberty, for the right to enjoy play and work without autocratic interference, and for freedom to develop and enjoy all the prosperity that the fertile earth offered. So it rings today, and will always ring in the hearts of free peoples.

It was a very fine way of celebrating a great day, and particularly for the lad who was able to have a part in it. No one thought about wasting money on fire crackers or popguns, or rockets, for the people of the colonies saw a long road ahead of them before they should be able to work out their independence. The call of the Liberty Bell was all the celebration they wanted or needed to start them along that road. The next year, though, saw them holding our flag. The Congress had adopted one, thirteen broad red and white stripes, and thirteen

mirth—*joy and laughter*
prosperity—*success*

autocratic interference—
government involvement

white stars, circled in a blue field, for the thirteen original American colonies, and waving for freedom.

Thinking It Through

1. Why did the boy in this story walk softly as he climbed the stairs to the belfry?

2. Name some of the men who were meeting in the statehouse.

3. What was the meeting about?

4. In what city did this meeting take place?

5. Who wrote and read the Declaration of Independence?

6. What did the boy and his grandfather do after Thomas Jefferson read the Declaration?

7. What was that bell called? Why was that a good name for the bell?